# Higher
# Technology & Design

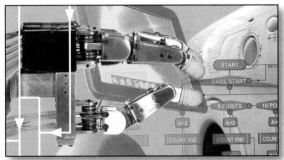

## Raymond Caldwell

Hodder & Stoughton

A MEMBER OF THE HODDER HEADLINE GROUP

**Acknowledgements**

The author is grateful to the following individuals and organisations for their support in the writing of this book:

Phyllis Caldwell without whose support this book would not have been possible. Denis Currie and Sydney Conn for their technical editing and photos of students' projects, Raymond Moffett for the photos of students' computer control projects. SMC Pneumatics for the illustrations and technical advice. A number of the electronic circuits and PCBs were developed using Crocodile Clips and PCB Wizard software.

Orders: please contact Bookpoint Ltd, 130 Milton Park, Abingdon, Oxon OX14 4SB. Telephone: (44) 01235 827720, Fax: (44) 01235 400454. Lines are open from 9.00–6.00, Monday to Saturday, with a 24 hour message answering service.

*British Library Cataloguing in Publication Data*
A catalogue record for this title is available from The British Library

ISBN 0 340 850 566

First published 2003
Impression number    10 9 8 7 6 5 4 3 2 1
Year                          2008  2007  2006 2005 2004 2003

Cover illustration by Zap Art.

Typeset by Fakenham Photosetting Ltd.

Printed in Italy for Hodder & Stoughton Educational, a division of Hodder Headline Plc, 338 Euston Road, London NW1 3BH.

# CONTENTS

# CHAPTER ONE

# Higher Electronics

## Darlington Pair Transistor

The Darlington pair is two transistors arranged so that the first one is used to turn on the second. By doing this you will have a circuit that is more responsive to small changes in the base current. This means that the output device will change from off to on more sharply.

The circuit shown in Figure 1.1 turns on a bulb when the temperature drops below a certain level. By using a Darlington pair, the bulb will glow brightly with a slight decrease in temperature. If a single transistor were used then the bulb would increase in brightness more slowly as the temperature fell.

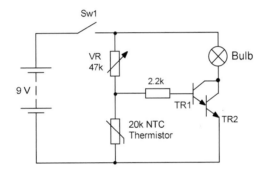

**Figure 1.1** *Darlington Pair circuit*

### How it works

When the temperature falls, the resistance of the thermistor increases. This forces the electrons down to the base of the first transistor TR1. TR1 is a BC109 and was selected because it has a high gain (hFE) of 200. This means, for every electron coming in at the base leg, 200 will pass through the collector-emitter. The 200 electrons are then offered to the base leg of the second transistor TR2. This has a gain of 40. You now have a total gain hFE of $200 \times 40 = 8000$.

A gain of 8000 will enable the small flow of electrons (current) coming in at the base of TR1 to be amplified twice causing a large flow of electrons through TR2. It is this large flow that makes the bulb glow brightly.

TR2 is a BFY51. This was chosen because, while it has a small gain in relation to TR1, it allows a large current, up to 1 amp, to pass through its collector-emitter.

It is possible to buy Darlington pair transistors in a single package such as the TIP121 that has a gain of 1000 and will allow up to 5 amps to pass trough its collector-emitter. A cheaper option is the

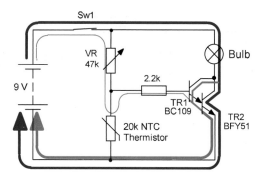

**Figure 1.2** *Flow of electrons through a Darlington pair circuit*

BCX38B that has a greater gain (hFE) of 2000. The drawback with the BCX38B is the amount of current it will allow to pass through it. This is only 800 mA. An advantage of using a single Darlington pair transistor is that the manufacturing of circuits is made easier. Also, the two transistors will be a matched pair for best results.

## Example — Soft drinks can light

### Design situation

Empty aluminium soft drink cans are often discarded after use. These can be recycled in a number of ways. Design a product for your bedroom that would incorporate one of these cans.

### Solution

In her final solution, the student designed an automatic night-light with increased sensitivity, shown in Figure 1.3. The circuit is housed inside the miniature soft drink can. The circuit and can are fixed to the acrylic stand by the toggle switch.

### How it works

The miniature LDR is fixed to the outside of the can. The LDR detects the falling light level and, when it is dark, the four ultra-bright LEDs come on. The LEDs will say on until it is light again.

**Figure 1.3** *Recycled soft drinks can being used as an automatic night-light*

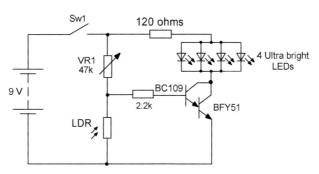

**Figure 1.5** *Circuit diagram for soft drinks can light*

### The circuit

Figure 1.5 shows the circuit diagram. A 9 volt PP3 battery powers the circuit. When the on/off switch (SW1) is closed, power goes to the circuit.

The miniature LDR (Light Dependent Resistor) is the sensor and its resistance will increase with darkness. The variable resistor allows you to set the sensitivity i.e., how dark it is before the LEDs come on.

### How the circuit is activated

When you close the on/off switch during the day, current flows from the battery down through the variable resistor to the LDR (red line in Figure 1.6). As the light is falling on the LDR it will have a very low resistance and act as a conductor. Current flows through it back to the battery.

**Figure 1.4** *Picture of the PCB and LED unit*

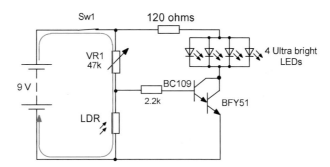

**Figure 1.6** *Path of current during the day*

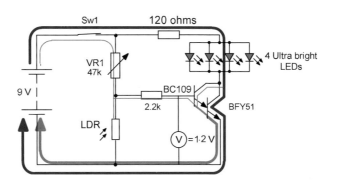

**Figure 1.7** *Path of the current at night*

In the dark, the LDR will have a very high resistance. This means the current cannot pass through it and must find another path back to the battery. It goes to the Darlington pair transistor, which acts as a very sensitive high-speed electronic switch. As the Darlington pair transistors turn on, current flows around the output part of the circuit. A 120 ohms ($\Omega$) resistor is used to reduce the current flowing through the LEDs to a safe level.

The path of the current flowing through the input/sensing part of the circuit (red) and the output part of the circuit (blue) is shown in Figure 1.7.

### Transistor base voltage

The voltage at the base of the first BC109 required to turn on the Darlington pair transistors must be between 1.2 volts and 1.6 volts. This is due to the arrangement of both transistors. The first transistor requires a voltage (force) greater than 0.6 volts for the electrons to penetrate its base layer. The base of the second transistor is fed from the emitter of the first and requires the another force of 0.6 volts for the electrons to penetrate the second base layer, making a combined force of at least 1.2 volts as shown in Figure 1.7.

# Ohm's Law

Electronics is concerned with the flow of electrons. The force that makes them flow we call voltage and it is measured in volts. The number of electrons passing a point in one second we call current and it is measured in amps, or more often in electronics we measure current in milliamps. A 1000 milliamps equals one amp. The electrons move along conductors and this is called the flow of current, but all conductors resist this flow to a greater or less degree, and we call this resistance. Resistance is measured in ohms or kilo ohms (1000 ohms).

Sometimes it is important to know how much current is flowing in your circuit. Too little and the circuit may not work. Too much and the circuit may be damaged. You may wish to know the resistance at a certain point in the circuit, or you may wish to know the voltage across two points (potential difference) at a certain point in your circuit. If you know two of the three variables: resistance, voltage or current, it is possible to calculate the remaining one. You can do this by using *Ohm's law*.

## Ohm's law states that

The resistance in ohms = voltage difference in volts/current in amps.
Or simply:
$R = V/I$    or $V = I \times R$     or $I = V/R$

## Notes on the soft drinks can night light

### LDR
The sensor was a miniature LDR. It was housed in a 5 mm LED bezel before passing it through a 6.5 mm hole in the side of the can.

### LEDs
Four 5mm red ultra-bright LEDs were connected in parallel. A 120 ohms current-limiting resistor was connected in series with the LEDs to protect them from too much current.

### Reflector
The LEDs were located in a 50 mm diameter 6 mm thick MDF disc that had a piece of silver foil glued to the outside (Figure 1.4). A 60 mm acrylic disc was fixed to the face of the foil. The completed reflector was an interference fitted into the top of the can.

### PCB
The size of the PCB must be no larger than 60 mm long by 30 mm wide, as it has to fit inside the can.

### Soft drinks can
A 150 ml soft drinks can was used to house the circuit. The top of the can was carefully removed by **gently** touching it against a moving abrasive belt on the linisher.

### Switch
A miniature toggle switch was fixed to the PCB with sold core wire, before being bent through 90°. The switch was then passed through a 6.5 mm hole in the base of the can, fixing the PCB to the base of the can.

### Battery
A PP3 battery was fixed to the back of the PCB using double-sided adhesive pads.

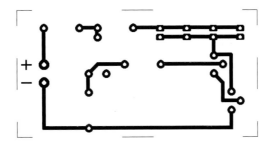

**Figure 1.8** *PCB mask for the soft drinks can night light*

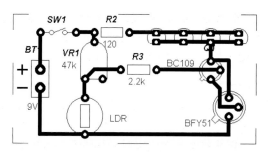

**Figure 1.9** *Silk screen for soft drinks can night light*

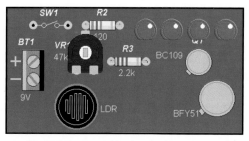

**Figure 1.10** *Top view of the PCB for soft drinks can night light*

## Components
4 × 5 mm red LEDs
1 × 2.2 k resistor
1 × 120 ohms resistor
1 × BC109 Transistor
1 × BFY51 Transistor
1 × 9 volt battery and battery clip
1 × PCB 60 mm × 30 mm
1 × Miniature LDR
1 × 47 k variable resistor
1 × SPST miniature toggle switch

# 555 timer circuits

The 555 timer is an integrated circuit (IC). It is used in electronic circuits when a precise timing period in required. Circuits incorporating the 555 IC will be consistently accurate. However, the maximum practical timing period for these circuits will be 20–25 minutes. If timing periods greater than this are attempted you will find that the resistors and capacitors you require become very high values and the poor tolerances of the large value capacitors will result in inaccurate timing periods.

## Pin layout and functions

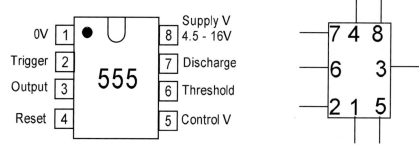

**Figure 1.11** *555 Pin layout and functions*

**Figure 1.12** *Graphic symbol for a 555 timer*

The 555 timer is an eight pin dual-in-line (DIL) IC. Each pin has a precise function to perform. The pin layout can be seen in Figure 1.11 and the functions are:

1. Pin 1 is at zero volts.
2. Pin 2 is the trigger. When the voltage at this pin falls below ⅓ of the supply voltage the timing cycle will start.
3. Pin 3 is the output. When this pin is on it will give an output voltage close to the supply voltage.
4. Pin 4 is the reset and can be used to reset the timing period back to the start.
5. Pin 5 is the control voltage.
6. Pin 6 is the threshold. When the voltage at this pin reaches ⅔ of the supply voltage it will end the timing period.
7. Pin 7 is the discharge or drain.
8. Pin 8 is the supply voltage pin. Most 555 timers will operate in the range 4.5 – 16 V.

## 555 monostable/astable circuits

555 timers can be used in two main ways.

- In a monostable circuit. This is a circuit with one stable state i.e. on or off. A 555 monostable circuit is one that turns on pin 3 for a set period of time before turning off and remaining off until pin 2 is pulled low again.
- In an astable circuit. Astable circuits continually change from off to on. A 555 astable circuit is one that continuously and automatically, turns off and on pin 3 for set periods of time.

## 555 timer monostable

The 555 monostable circuit can be used when you want the output to come on for a period of time and then go off.

Figure 1.13 shows a drawing of a project designed by a student as the means of setting the time period for 'moves' in the game of chess. The circuit incorporated a 555 monostable. To start the time period the push-to-make switch is pressed. This provides a low signal at pin 2, which brings on an LED for the selected time. When the time is up the LED goes out.

**Figure 1.13** *Drawing of a chess move timer*

The circuit diagram for the project is shown in Figure 1.14.

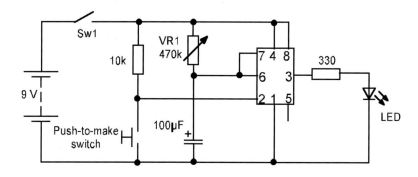

**Figure 1.14** *555 monostable circuit*

### How it works

To explain how it works it is worth considering the function of each of the pins.

### Adding power to the chip

All ICs require power to make them function. The 555 timer is no exception. The positive is connected to pin 8 and the negative to pin 1. Pin 4 is a reset and is not used in this case. However, you will still need to connect it to the positive rail to make the circuit work. This is shown in Figure 1.15.

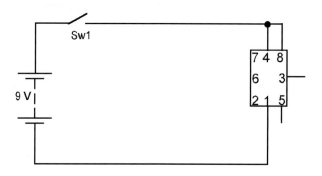

**Figure 1.15** *Connecting the power*

### Connecting the output pin 3

The objective of this circuit is to turn on an output device for a set period.

The output in this case is an LED with its 330 ohms current limiting resistor. These are connected to pin 3. This is shown in Figure 1.16.

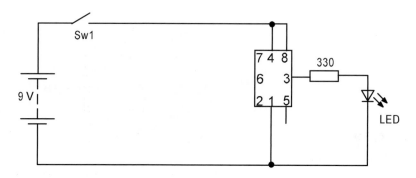

**Figure 1.16** *Connecting the output. Pin 3*

### Starting the timing cycle pin 2

When pin 2 is low (less than ⅓ the supply voltage) the timing cycle will start. The most common way to do this is to connect a push-to-make switch between pin 2 and zero volts. Pin 2 must be tied high through a 10 k resistor. This will keep the output low (off) until you press the push- to-make switch. This is shown in Figure 1.17.

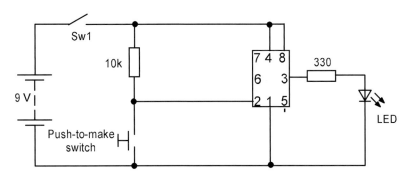

**Figure 1.17** *Starting the timing cycle. Pin 2*

### Achieving the on time. Pin 6

Once the timing cycle has started, it should stop after the desired time period has passed. To achieve this you will need to connect a resistor and capacitor to pin 6 as shown. The capacitor fill rate is determined by the size of the resistor. When the voltage present at pin 6 has reached ⅔ of the supply voltage, the time on period will end. This is shown in Figure 1.18.

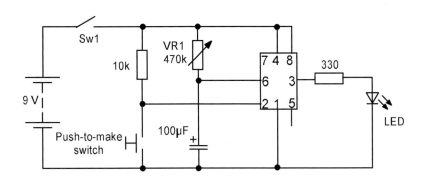

**Figure 1.18** *Achieving the on time. Pin 6*

### Discharging the capacitor. Pin 7

To enable the timing cycle to be repeated, it will be necessary to discharge the capacitor through pin 7. This is shown in Figure 1.19.

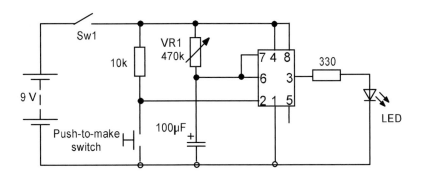

**Figure 1.19**

*Discharging the capacitor. Pin 7*

### Turning the output off for a time period

It is possible to have the output constantly on and then turn off for the time period. To do this, connect your output to the supply rail then down into pin 3.

Once the push-to-make switch is pressed, the LED will turn off. This is shown in Figure 1.20.

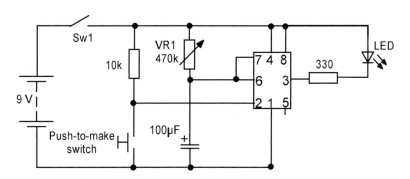

**Figure 1.20** *Turning the output off for a time period*

### Adding a reset

By connecting a push-to-make switch between pin 4 and the supply rail you can reset the 555 timer at any moment in its cycle.

The addition of a reset switch to the circuit is shown in Figure 1.21. If no reset switch is required, pin 4 must be connected to the supply rail to ensure that the 555 timer resets itself at the end of a timing period.

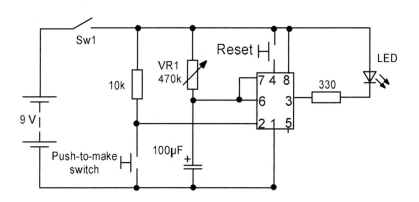

**Figure 1.21** *Adding a reset switch. Pin 4*

### Connecting output devices

If the output device you are connecting to the 555 timer requires a large amount of current, the 555 will be unable to operate it directly. The 555, like most ICs, is very good at giving you an output voltage close to the supply voltage, but the current will be very small. For outputs other than LEDs and other small current devices you will need to amplify the output current.

The simplest way to amplify the output current is to add a transistor to the circuit and use this to drive your output device. An example of this is shown in Figure 1.22.

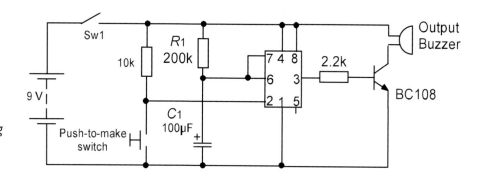

**Figure 1.22** *Amplifying the output current using a transistor*

## Game timer using the 555 monostable circuit off-on-off

### How it works

The circuit shown in Figure 1.22 will come on when pin 2 is low. It will remain on until the voltage at pin 6 reaches ⅔ of the supply voltage. As the supply voltage is 9 V, pin 6 will have to be just above 6 V. The length of time it takes for this to happen will depend on the length of time it takes to fill the capacitor. Once pin 6 is greater than 6 V the output goes off and the capacitor starts to drain through pin 7 and pin 1. This leaves the capacitor empty, waiting for the next input signal at pin 2.

### Calculating T

Formula for calculating the length of time that the LED is on:

$T = R1 \times C1$ seconds

After the 555 has been triggered by pressing the push-to-make switch, the buzzer will come on. As $T = R1 \times C1$ then time on will depend on the value of these two components. The value of $R1$ is given in ohms and the value of $C1$ in farads. If you consider the circuit in Figure 1.22 then:

$R1 = 200,000$ (200 k)
$C1 = 0.0001$ (100 uF)

$T$ can be found by: $T = R1 \times C1$ seconds
$T = 200,000 \times 0.0001$
$T = 20$ seconds

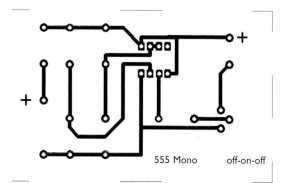

**Figure 1.23** *PCB for 555 monostable timer*

555 Mono          off-on-off

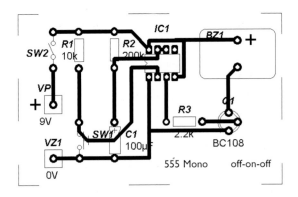

**Figure 1.24** *Silk Screen for 555 monostable timer*

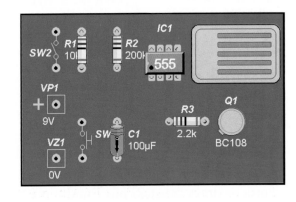

**Figure 1.25** *Top View of the PCB for 555 monostable timer*

### Waveform for the 555 monostable

$T$ = the time on in seconds.

**Figure 1.26** *Waveform for a 555 timer*

### Bill of materials for 555 monostable

1 × 100 μF electrolytic capacitor
1 × 10 k resistor
1 × 200 k resistor
1 × 2.2 k resistor
1 × 555 timer IC
1 × BC108 transistor
1 × 6 volt buzzer
1 × Miniature SPST toggle switch
1 × Push-to-make switch
1 × Board 76 mm × 48 mm

## Game timer using the *555* monostable circuit on-off-on

### Design situation

During the game of chess each player is allowed a set time to make his or her move.

### Design brief

Design an electronic game timer that will tell the player that the allocated time period has expired.

### Solution

The final design solution uses an electronic 555 monostable timer circuit as shown in Figure 1.27. This gave an on-off-on pattern to the output. Conventional 555 monostable circuits such as shown in Figure 1.22 come on then go off. When playing chess this was a distraction. To overcome this problem, a PNP transistor was used.

## Output transistor

The PNP transistor connected to pin 3 is shown in Figure 1.26. This replaced the standard BC108 NPN transistor. NPN Transistors come on when the voltage at the base is greater than 0.6 volts while the PNP does the opposite; they turn off when a voltage greater than 0.6 volts is present at the base. A BC178 general purpose PNP transistor was used in this circuit.

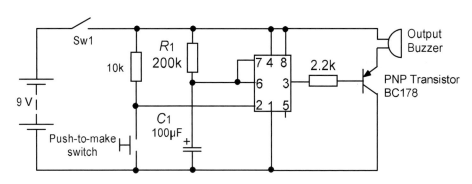

**Figure 1.27** *555 monostable timer circuit diagram with a PNP transistor*

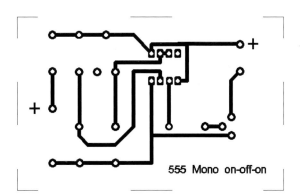

**Figure 1.28** *PCB Mask for the 555 monostable timer on-off-on*

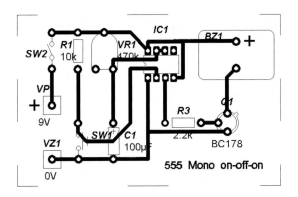

**Figure 1.29** *Silk screen for the 555 monostable timer on-off-on*

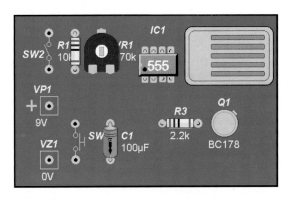

**Figure 1.30** *Top view of the board*

### Bill of materials for 555 monostable

1 × 100 µF electrolytic capacitor
1 × 10 k resistor
1 × 200 k resistor
1 × 2.2 k resistor
1 × 555 timer IC
1 × BC178 PNP transistor
1 × 6 volt buzzer
1 × Miniature SPST toggle switch
1 × Push-to-make switch
1 × Board 76 mm × 48 mm

**Example**

## 555 astable timer

A 555 astable circuit is one where the output turns on and off continuously. In this circuit pin 2, the trigger, and pin 6, the threshold, are connected together. When the voltage at pin 2 is less than ⅓ of the supply, the output will come on. This will remain on until the voltage present at pin 6 is just greater than ⅔ the supply voltage. At this moment the output will turn off. This happens repeatedly until the circuit is turned off at SW1.

### How it works

The current flows from the battery down through $R1 + R2$ to fill the capacitor. At this point pin 2 is low and the output is on. Pin 6 will wait until the charge in the capacitor is just greater than 6 volts at which point it turns the output at pin 3 off. It is at this

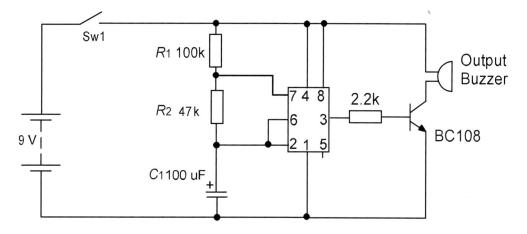

**Figure 1.31** *555 astable timer circuit*

moment the capacitor starts to drain through pin 7 and pin 1. The rate of drain is determined by the value of *C*1 and *R*2. Pin 2 is constantly reading the voltage in the capacitor. When the voltage falls below ⅓ of the supply voltage the output at pin 3 will come back on. The circuit is shown in Figure 1.31.

### Waveform for the 555 astable

The output waveform for a 555 astable circuit is square wave.

In Figure 1.32, *t*1 will be the time on and *t*2 the time off, *t*1 + *t*2 = the frequency in hertz where 1 Hz is equal to one second.

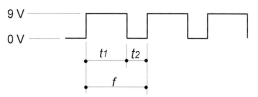

**Figure 1.32** *555 astable timer frequency*

### Calculating frequency

Formula for calculating the *frequency:*

$f = t1 + t2$
$t1 = 0.7 \times (R1 + R2) \times C1$
$t2 = 0.7 \times R2 \times C1$

### PCB for a 555 astable circuit

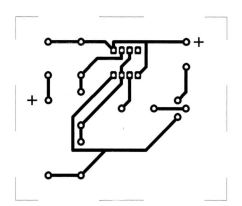

**Figure 1.33** *Artwork for 555 astable circuit*

**Figure 1.34** *Silk screen for 555 astable circuit*

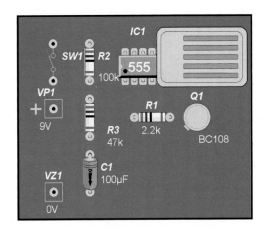

**Figure 1.35** *Top view of the PCB for 555 astable circuit*

### Bill of materials for 555 Astable Circuit

1 × 100 μF electrolytic capacitor
1 × 47 k resistor
1 × 100 k resistor
1 × 2.2 k resistor
1 × 555 IC
1 × BC108 transistor
1 × 6 volt buzzer
1 × SPST toggle switch
1 × Board 68.6 × 60

### 555 Timer circuits. Author's notes

There are a number of different types of 555 ICs on the market. The most commonly used is the CMOS ICM7555 type. As they do not draw nearly as much current as the older NE555 type, this should make your battery last longer.

### Accuracy

The problem will be in calculating the timing cycle. The standard resistor will have a 2–5% tolerance, while capacitors tolerances could be as poor as 50%. Electrolytic capacitors have the poorest tolerances of all and these tend to be what most students use for long time delays. This makes precise calculations difficult. However, once you have your 555 built and running, the timing cycle will be constant every time. For this reason it is sometimes helpful to make one of your resistors a variable resistor, so that you can set a precise time period.

### Dual 555 ICs

555 ICs come in standard 8 DIL packages. You can also purchase a dual 555 timer that has two 555 ICs in one 16 pin DIL package. These are called 556 dual timers and are very useful for circuits where two 555 circuits are built into the one circuit. The circuit shown in Figure 1.36 used two 555 timer ICs. These could be replaced with a single 556 dual timer IC to simplify construction and save space on the PCB.

**Display Stand**

### Design situation

A jeweller displays watches on a stand that sits on the shop counter. Watches can be displayed only on one side of the stand. He would like a display stand that attracts the customer's attention and shows a greater number of watches.

### Solution

The final solution was a rotating display stand. The stand would rotate for 42 seconds, stop for 14 seconds and repeat this for 30 minutes.

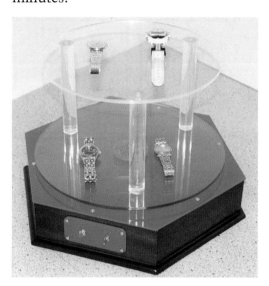

**Figure 1.36** *Photo of the rotating display stand*

### How it works

The stand has a two-tier clear acrylic display unit that is attached to a small gearbox that is driven by a small d.c. electric motor. The turning on and off of the motor is achieved by means of a relay that is the final output stage of two 555 timer circuits.

The first stage is a 555-monostable circuit stays on for 30 minutes. This supplies power to the second stage, which is a 555-astable circuit that comes on for 42 seconds then goes off for 14 seconds. The third and final stage is the relay that controls the motor.

### Circuit diagram

The circuit was powered by means of a PP3 battery while two 1.5 volt batteries powered the d.c. motor. A relay was used for the final output to the motor. This isolated the motor from the circuit as feedback from the motor was found to be causing the timing parts of the circuit to malfunction.

## Combining a *555* monostable with a *555* astable

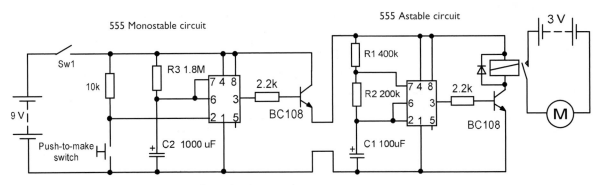

**Figure 1.37** *Circuit for the jewellery display stand*

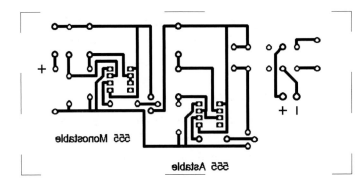

**Figure 1.38** *PCB for the jewellery display stand*

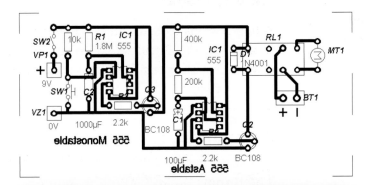

**Figure 1.39** *Silk screen for the jewellery display stand*

**Figure 1.40** *Top view of the PCB for the jewellery display stand*

## Design project warning triangle

The warning triangle was part of a student's GCSE project that incorporated a 555 astable circuit.

### Design Situation

When a car breaks down at night on dark country roads there is the constant danger from other road users. The oncoming traffic

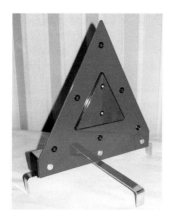

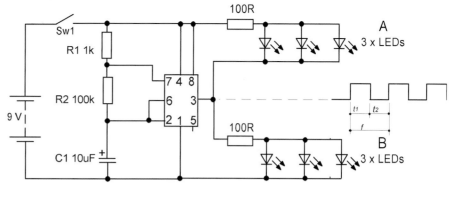

**Figure 1.42** *555 astable circuit diagram for the Warning Triangle*

may not know you are there until it is too late. There is a need for a warning triangle that will warn other road users of the unforeseen danger ahead.

### Solution

The circuit incorporated a 555 astable that flashed, in sequence, two sets of three LEDs. The front and rear views of the finished product is shown in Figure 1.41

**Figure 1.41** *Picture showing front and rear views of the warning triangle*

## How it works

When SW1 is closed, pin 2 is low which causes pin 3 on the 555 to go high. Pin 3 will remain high until the electrons flowing down through $R1$ and $R2$ provide enough charge at the capacitor $C1$, to produce 6 V at pin 6. When pin 6 reaches this threshold level the output at pin 3 goes low.

During the time pin 3 is high, current will flow from the pin to the negative rail. This will bring on the three bottom LEDs at B. This is shown in Figure 1.43

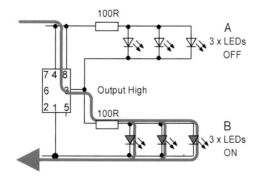

**Figure 1.43** *Bottom LEDs on when pin 3 is high*

### Pin 3 Low

During the time pin 3 is low current can flow through the LEDs along route A. When this happens the top LEDs will be on. This is shown in Figure 1.44

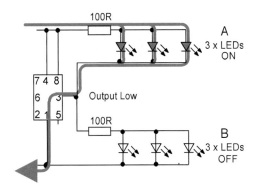

**Figure 1.44** *Top LEDs on when pin 3 low*

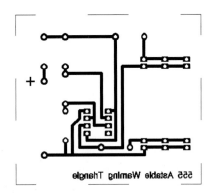

**Figure 1.45** *PCB for the Warning Triangle*

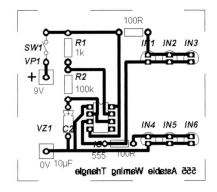

**Figure 1.46** *Silk screen for the warning triangle*

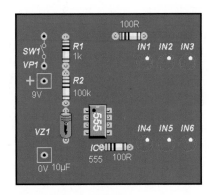

**Figure 1.47** *Top view of the PCB for the warning triangle*

***Bill of materials for the 555 astable circuit used for the warning triangle***

1 × 10 µF electrolytic capacitor
1 × 1 k resistor
1 × 100 k resistor
2 × 100 R resistor
1 × 555 timer IC
6 × Red LEDs
1 × SPST miniature toggle switch
1 × Board 66 mm × 58 mm

# Potential divider

A potential divider is not a circuit in its own right, but is a building block for other circuits. The purpose of the potential divider is to reduce the voltage present at any point in a circuit down to the required level. The following examples show how the potential divider works

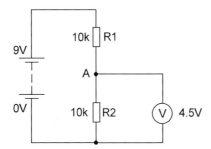

**Figure 1.48** *Potential divider with equal value resistors*

When 9 V is present between the positive and negative rails, then by using two resistors of **equal value** it is possible to divide the voltage into two equal parts. In Figure 1.48, *R*1 is equal to *R*2 so the voltage drop across each resistor is 4.5 V.

In figure 1.49 *R*1 is greater than *R*2 so the voltage drop will be greatest through *R*1. Therefore, the output voltage between 'A' and the negative rail will be less than half of the supply. In the example shown in Figure 1.49 it is 3 V. All the voltage will drop across both resistors in this circuit.

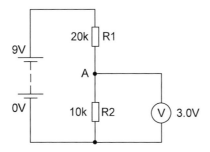

**Figure 1.49** *Potential divider with unequal value resistors*

## Calculating voltage drop

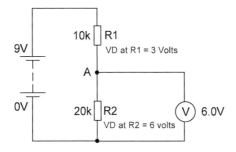

**Figure 1.50** *Calculating voltage drop across R1*

Voltage drop across a resistor in a potential divider can be found by using the following formula:

$$\text{Voltage drop across } R1 = \frac{R1 \times V}{(R1 + R2)}$$

$$\text{VD across } R1 = \frac{10 \times 9}{(10 + 20) \times 1}$$

$$VD \text{ across } R1 = \frac{10 \times 9}{30 \times 1} = \frac{90}{30} = \frac{3}{1}$$

Voltage drop across $R1 = 3\,V$

### Calculating the current gain of a bipolar transistor

A small amount of current offered to the base of a transistor will enable a larger current to pass through the collector and out of the emitter. The increase in current or gain will depend on the transistor selected.

$h$FE (is the current gain)
$I$c (is the collect current)
$I$b (is the collect base)

If you know two of the variables you can calculate the third by using the formula:

$$h\text{FE} = \frac{\text{steady collector current}}{\text{steady base current}}$$

$$h\text{FE} = \frac{I\text{c}}{I\text{b}}$$

When calculating the transistor gain of the BC108 transistor used in the night light circuit shown in Figure 1.51, an ammeter was connected in series with the collector and another connected in series with the base. A current reading of 37.7 mA was recorded at the collector and 0.377 mA at the base.

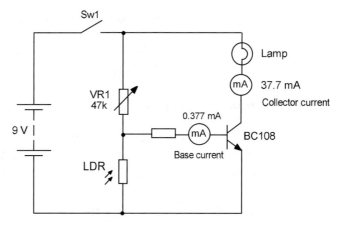

**Figure 1.51** *Night Light circuit*

### Calculating the transistor gain

$$h\text{FE} = \frac{I\text{c}}{I\text{b}}$$

$$h\text{FE} = \frac{37.7\text{mA}}{0.37\text{mA}}$$

$$h\text{FE} = 100$$

The BC108 transistor used in this circuit had a current gain ($h$FE) of 100.

# Operational amplifier as a comparator

The operational amplifiers, or op amps as they are called, are ICs used to amplify small differences in voltage. The IC is housed in an 8 pin DIL package (DIL stands for dual-in-line) and because of their wide use in a whole range of applications, millions are produced every year. This mass production makes the operational amplifier a relatively low cost and useful component.

The scope of this section will be to consider the op amp as a sensing comparator in control circuits.

There are a number of different makes and types of op amps to choose from. Experience has shown that the CA3140 is a good choice when the op amp has to function as a comparator. Therefore the CA3140 will be used throughout this chapter.

Coming to terms with the CA3140 op amp as a comparator should be a relatively straightforward. Its main function is to compare the voltages at pins 2 and 3 and provide the relative output. When pin 2 is higher than pin 3 the output is low but if pin 3 is the highest then the output is high.

### Identifying the CA3140

The CA3140 is housed in an 8 pin DIL package. Pin number one is beside the small dot at the top of the package or at the top left corner if the package has a U-shaped cut-out. The identification of pin 1 is shown in Figure 1.52.

### Graphic symbol for an op amp

This is a small triangle with the two inputs and the output drawn on. This is shown in Figure 1.53.

### Package diagrams

Sometimes you may see the package with the symbol drawn on top. This can be helpful to you when identifying the pin layout for a specific IC. This is shown in Figure 1.52.

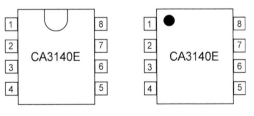

**Figure 1.52** *Identifying pin 1*

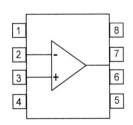

**Figure 1.53** *Graphic symbol and package diagram for an op amp*

### Pin identification

Pin 1: Offset null (not required for this module)
Pin 2: Inverting input ($-$)
Pin 3: Non-inverting input ($+$)

Pin 4: Negative

Pin 5: Offset null (not required for this module)

Pin 6: Output

Pin 7: Positive supply

Pin 8: Not connected

Pins 1,5,8 are not used

## Light sensing circuit

The circuit in figure 1.54 shows and op amp used to turn on a bulb when there is a small change in the amount of light falling on the LDR.

## Designing the op amp circuit shown in Figure 1.54

### Connecting the output

As with all op amp ICs, the objective is to turn on an output. The CA3140E has pin 6 as its output.

When the output is high (on) the voltage will be very close to the supply voltage but, as with most ICs, the current will be small. The purpose of the BC108 transistor is to amplify the output current.

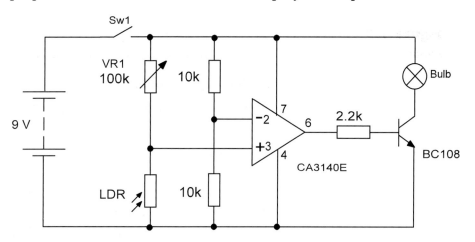

**Figure 1.54** *Light sensing circuit*

### Adding the reference voltage to pin 2

When the op amp is being used as a comparator you will need to set a reference voltage at either pin 2 or pin 3. In this example, pin 2 has been set as the reference voltage.

The two 10 k resistors act as a potential divider. As both resistors are the same value then the voltage drop across each will be 4.5 V resulting in 4.5 V being present at pin 2. This is referred to as the reference voltage and is shown in Figure 1.56.

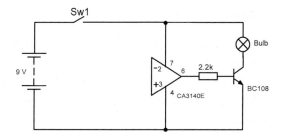

**Figure 1.55** *Output pin 6*

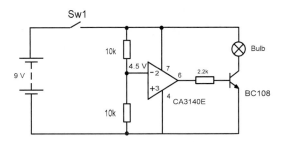

**Figure 1.56** *Setting the reference voltage at 4.5 V*

### Adding the sensor to the op amp circuit

VR1 and the LDR provide the second potential divider. VR1 is set so that the voltage at pin 3 is just below that of pin 2. This is shown in Figure 1.57. A slight increase in resistance at the LDR due to falling light levels will increase the voltage at pin 3. When this is higher than 4.5 V, pin 6 will go high, turning on the output.

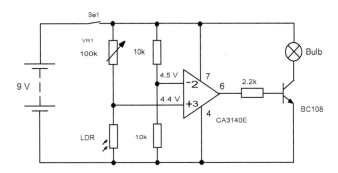

**Figure 1.57** *Adding the sensor*

### Positioning the output device

When the bulb is connected to the circuit it will come on when pin 6 is high.

It is good practice to connect your output device between the emitter and negative rail as the op amp may also be on when the output is low. This is due to the internal structure of the op amp that enables pin 6 to conduct via pin 4 to the negative rail when no output signal is present at pin 6. This is shown in Figure 1.58.

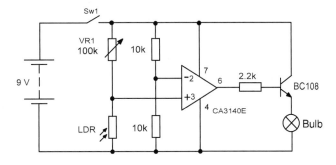

**Figure 1.58** *Placing the output below the transistor*

### Frost alarm circuit

In this circuit a 15k NTC thermistor and 47k variable resistor form the sensing part of the circuit. As the temperature falls the resistance of the thermistor rises increasing the voltage at pin 3. When this rises above the voltage present at pin 2 the buzzer will sound.

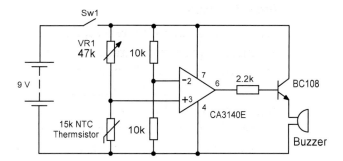

**Figure 1.59** *Frost alarm circuit*

## Greenhouse environmental control project

The op amp is very useful in situations where a rapid response is required to maintain the precise control of an environment.

### Design situation

The temperature inside a greenhouse can rise very quickly on sunny days. While most greenhouses have opening windows to allow for ventilation in these conditions, they do require the owner to be present to operate them. Therefore, there is a need for an automatic window opener that will enable ventilation of the greenhouse while the owner is out.

### Solution

The solution involved the use of an input thermistor forming part of the potential divider that controlled the voltage at pin 3. The thermistor chosen was a negative temperature coefficient (NTC). This is one where the resistance decreases with heat. The thermistor was positioned at the top of a potential divider so that a falling resistance due to an increase in temperature would result in a rising voltage at pin 3. This is shown in Figure 1.60.

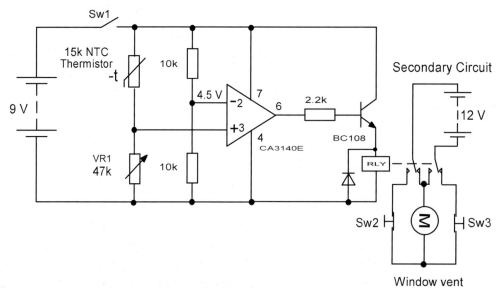

**Figure 1.60** *Automatic window opener for a greenhouse*

### How it works

As the temperature increases, the resistance of the thermistor falls. As this happens the voltage at pin 3 will rise. VR1 is used to set the sensitivity at pin 3 enabling it to be just above the voltage at pin 2 at the required temperature. When the voltage at pin 3 is higher than pin 2 then the output at pin 6 will be on. This will enable the relay to come on and complete the secondary circuit causing the motor to turn clockwise. The rotating motor opens the window. When the temperature in the greenhouse falls below the set limit, the relay turns off causing the motor to turn anti-clockwise, closing the window. The push-to-break limit switches SW2 and 3, cut the power to the motor when the window has reached the opening or closing limits.

| Example | **Improving greenhouse environment control design** |
|---|---|

The automatic window opener circuit used in Figure 1.60 opened the window when the temperature inside the greenhouse reached a set limit and closed it when the temperature dropped. When this was installed it worked perfectly to reduce the temperature inside the greenhouse. While this solved the problem of overheating, the problem of low temperatures and night frost still remained. It was decided to add a second op amp circuit to the product. This was to control a 12 V heat lamp that would come on when the temperature fell below a predetermined level. The second op amp circuit is shown in Figure 1.61.

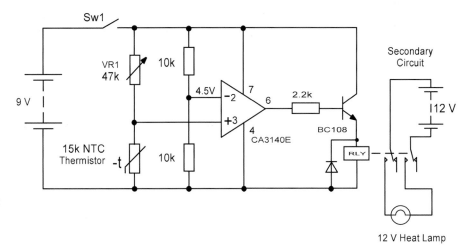

**Figure 1.61** *Automatic heat lamp circuit for a greenhouse*

### How it works

As the temperature falls, the resistance of the thermistor increases. This decreases the flow of electrons through it forcing them down to pin 3 on the op amp. When the flow reaches a force (voltage) greater than the 4.5 V reference voltage, set at pin 2, the output at pin 6 will go high. This high will enable the relay to come on completing the secondary heat lamp circuit. The heat lamp will stay on until the temperature in the greenhouse rises above the predetermined limit.

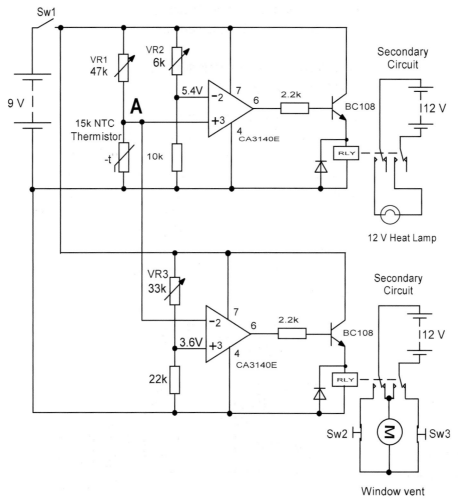

**Figure 1.62** *Combined heat lamp and window vent circuits*

### Adding lag to the greenhouse environment control designs

By combining the two circuits shown in Figures 1.60 and 1.61, it is possible to create *lag* in the system. This enabled the heat lamp to come on below 10°C and stay on until the temperature increased above that level again. The window vent was set to come on above 25°C and stay open until the temperature decreased to below that level. When the temperature in the greenhouse was between 10 and 24°C both secondary systems were off. This is what is known as '*lag*' in the circuit or a period of waiting between the two states. The combined circuit is shown in Figure 1.62

### How it works

The single thermistor controls the voltage going to both op amps. As the resistance at the thermistor increases and decreases, the voltage at point 'A' is sent to both op amps. Each compares this to the preset reference voltage and responds accordingly. By setting the reference at pin 2 on the op amp for the heat lamp circuit to 5.4 V, the lamp came on when the temperature fell below 10°C. On the window vent circuit, pin 3 was set to a reference voltage 3.6 V. When the temperature increased to more than 25°C, the window vent opened.

## Author's notes for the greenhouse environment control project

The components used were all standard components with the exception of the fan and heater. These were both bought from a caravan equipment supply company and were powered by a 12 V car battery. The calibration of both circuits was achieved by placing the thermistor into a box with a thermometer. Ice was placed in the box until the correct minimum temperature was reached. At this point the VR3 and VR1 were adjusted to bring on the heat lamp. The ice was removed and a lamp placed in the box. When the correct temperature was reached, VR2 was then adjusted to turn on the motor.

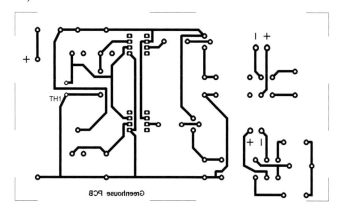

**Figure 1.63** *PCB greenhouse environment control project*

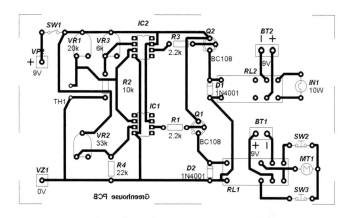

**Figure 1.64** *Silk screen greenhouse environment control project*

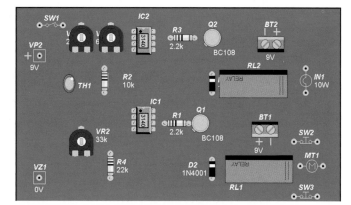

**Figure 1.65** *Top view of the pcb greenhouse environment control project*

### Bill of materials

1 × 10 k resistor
2 × 2.2 k resistors
1 × 22 k resistor
2 × IN4001 diode
1 × 22 k preset
2 × 47 k preset
2 × CA3140E op amp IC
2 × BC108 transistors
1 × Disk thermistor NTC
2 × DPDT relays
2 × Push-to-break switches
1 × 12 V heat lamp
1 × 12 V D.C. motor

# Single and dual power supplies used with op amps

Op amps are made to operate from either single or dual power supply voltages. The single power supply connection is straightforward. Pin 7 is connected to the positive supply rail and pin 4 to the negative rail. This is shown in Figure 1.66. The output voltage from pin 6 will be between zero voltage and that available from the supply rail, in this case 9 V.

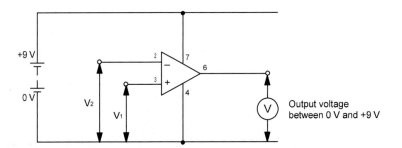

**Figure 1.66** *Single power supply to the op amp*

## Dual power supplies

It is possible to design your circuit so that it will operate with a dual power supply. The advantage of this is that the output can be between 0 V and + 9 V or 0 V and − 9 V. This is shown in Figure 1.67.

## Why do op amps have two inputs?

For the op amp to function as an amplifier it needs two input voltages, one at pin 2 (the inverting pin) and one at pin 3 (non-inverting pin). When the voltage at pin 3 is greater than pin 2 the output voltage at pin 6 will be positive i.e. between 0 V and + 9 V for the circuit shown in Figure 1.68. In this state the output signal is said to be non-inverted i.e. the same as the positive input voltage. When the voltage at pin 2 is greater than pin 3 then the output voltage at pin 6 will be negative i.e. between 0 V and −9 V for the circuit shown in Figure 1.69. In this state the output signal is said to be inverted, the opposite to the positive supply voltage.

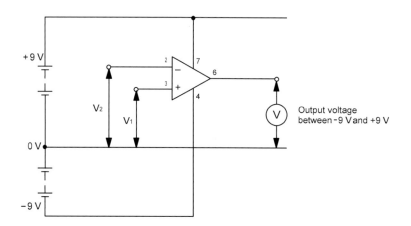

**Figure 1.67** *Dual power supply to the op amp*

## How a dual power supply op amp works

When you use a dual power supply it is possible to have the current flowing out from pin 6 along to 0 volts. This will happen when the voltage at pin 3 is greater than pin 2. When this happens, current will flow out of the top battery into pin 7 and out of pin 6 to 0 volts.

### Turning on the red LED

When an LED is placed between pin 6 and 0 volts this will come on, as the voltage at pin 3 is greater than pin 2. This is shown in Figure 1.68.

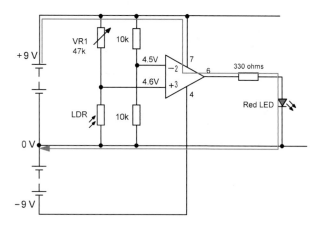

**Figure 1.68** *Flow of current when the voltage at pin 3 is greater than pin 2*

### Turning on the green LED

It is also possible to have the current flowing from 0 volts into pin 6 out of pin 4 down to −9 V. When the voltage at pin 2 is greater than the voltage at pin 3, then pin 6 is low. This will allow current to flow from bottom battery along the 0 V rail up through the green LED into pin 6 and out of pin 4 down to the negative side of the bottom battery labelled −9 V. This is shown in Figure 1.69.

31

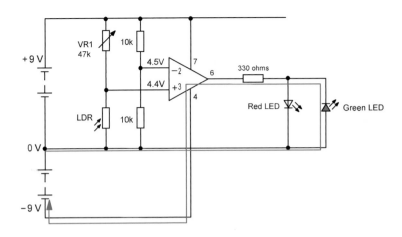

**Figure 1.69** *Flow of current when the voltage at pin 2 is greater than pin 3*

## Moisture Sensing Circuit

A dual power op amp can be used to detect small changes in resistance on either side of the reference voltage and signal the changes.

### Design situation

The soil used for house plants need to be kept wet if the plant is to survive. Often it is difficult to know whether to water them or not. The design brief was for a moisture-sensing device that will detect small changes in resistance in the soil due to the amount of moisture present in the soil and indicate when the soil is wet or dry.

**Figure 1.70** *Picture of house plant*

### Solution

The final solution was a vacuum formed plastic box containing the dual power supply op amp circuit. Two copper rods acting as probes were pushed into the soil to detect the amount of moisture present. This is shown in Figure 1.71.

### Circuit diagram

The op amp circuit is powered by a dual power supply. The two PP3 batteries are arranged in series to give $+9\,V$ to $-9\,V$. A drawing of the two batteries connected in series is shown in Figure 1.72.

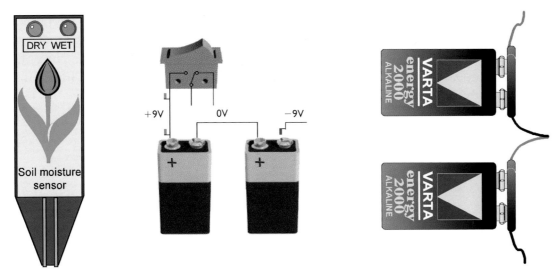

**Figure 1.71** *Drawing of the soil moisture sensor*

**Figure 1.72** *Positive and negative supply*

The voltage at pin 2 is called the reference voltage. By using two resistors of the same value (10k) this has been set at 4.5 V. This is shown in Figure 1.73.

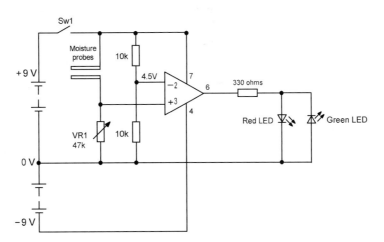

**Figure 1.73** *Circuit diagram for the soil moisture sensor*

There are two output LEDs. The red LED comes on when the soil is wet. This happens as the current is flowing across the wet soil between the probes supplying a voltage at pin 3 that is greater than pin 2. At this point the current will flow out of pin 6 through the red LED to 0 V.

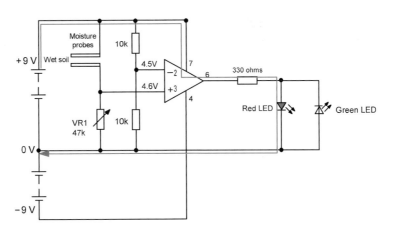

**Figure 1.74** *Flow of current when the soil is wet*

33

The green LED comes on when the soil is dry. This happens because the resistance across the probes is high, thus producing a low voltage at pin 3. This turns off pin 6 allowing the current to flow from the second battery up into the green LED into pin 6 and out of pin 4. This is shown in Figure 1.75.

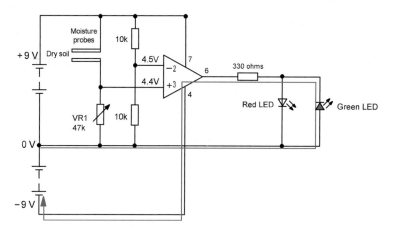

**Figure 1.75** *Flow of current when the soil is dry*

## Notes on the soil moisture sensor
### Op amp

A 741 op amp was found to be suitable for the project as the 741 functions well when used as an inverting and non-inverting op amp.

### Batteries

Two PP3 batteries were used, although these took up a lot of space and made the project larger than intended. Later it was found that two L1028 12 V alkaline batteries required less space and, by changing the 330 $\Omega$ resistor to 470 $\Omega$, the circuit worked fine.

### Setting the sensitivity

A 47k variable resistor was placed in series with the probes. By turning this it was possible to set the sensitivity of the circuit. You may wish to change the value of the variable resistor to suit your specific plant.

### Probes

These were made from 3 mm brass rods threaded at the end. The probes were fixed to the plastic vacuum box by means of two 3 mm nuts and washers. The distance between the probes was 10 mm but this space depended upon the type of plant and how wet the soil had to be.

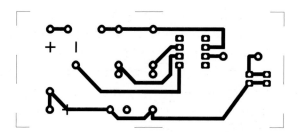

**Figure 1.76** *PCB for a soil moisture sensor*

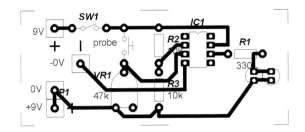

**Figure 1.77** *Silk screen for a soil moisture sensor*

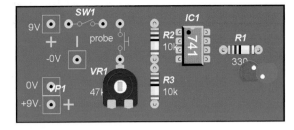

**Figure 1.78** *Top view of the PCB for a soil moisture sensor*

### Bill of materials

2 × PP3 batteries
2 × 10k resistors
1 × 330 ohms resistor
1 × SPST miniature toggle switch
1 × 47k variable preset resistor
1 × green LED
1 × red LED
1 × 741 op amp
2 × 40 mm long × 3 mm diameter brass rods
4 × 3 mm brass nuts and washers
1 × PCB 70 mm × 30 mm

# The operational amplifier used as a voltage amplifiers

In the last section on comparators, the op amp was used as a high-speed switch where a slight difference in input voltages would cause the output to instantly go high or low. Op amps are capable of amplifying the voltage difference between pin 2 and 3 by in excess of 100 000 times. This being the case, the voltage at pin 3 only needs to be 1 mA larger than that of pin 2 for the output to come fully on. For example, the gain of a 741 op amp for d.c. signals is about 100 000. For practical purposes you may not need or want the gain to be as great as this, so you will need to control the gain.

### Controlling the gain of the op amp

The gain of an op amp can be controlled by using a feedback resistor RF. The relationship between RF and RIN will determine the voltage gain present at the output. The arrangement of these resistors is shown in Figure 1.79. When you are feeding back to the inverting pin of the op amp, this is referred to as 'controlling the gain of an inverting negative feedback voltage amplifier op amp'.

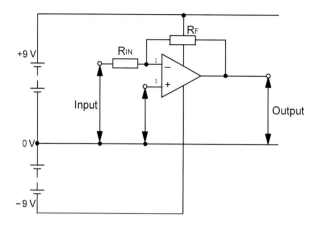

**Figure 1.79** *Controlling the gain of an inverting negative feedback voltage amplifier op amp*

### *The formula for calculating voltage gain of an op amp*

$$\text{Voltage gain} = \frac{\text{value of the feedback resistor } R_F}{\text{value of the input resistor } R_{IN}}$$

If $R_F$ has a value of 200k and $R_{IN}$ 10k then the output would have a gain 20 times greater than the input. As the output signal is inverted, then the gain is expressed as $-20$.

## Negative feedback voltage amplifiers

There are two basic versions of the **negative feedback** voltage amplifier:

- Inverting negative feedback voltage amplifier. This is shown in Figure 1.79.
- Non-inverting negative feedback voltage amplifier. This is shown in Figure 1.80.

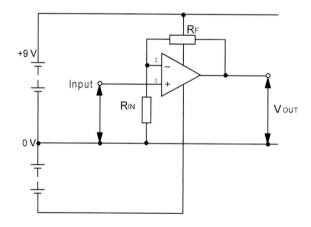

**Figure 1.80** *Non-inverting negative feedback voltage amplifier*

### Calculating the voltage gain for an inverting negative feedback voltage amplifier

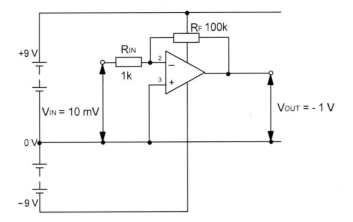

**Figure 1.81** *Inverting negative feedback voltage amplifier*

Voltage gain, $A_{\mathrm{Vel}} = - R_{\mathrm{F}}/R_{\mathrm{IN}}$

$$A_{\mathrm{Vel}} = V_{\mathrm{out}}/V_{\mathrm{in}} = - \frac{R_{\mathrm{F}}}{R_{\mathrm{IN}}} = - \frac{100\ \mathrm{k}}{1\ \mathrm{k}} = -100$$

Therefore, in a circuit where the input voltage is 10 mV

$$\begin{aligned} V\mathrm{out} \ &= - V_{\mathrm{IN}} \times 100 \\ &= - 10\ \mathrm{mV} \times 100 \\ &= - 1000\ \mathrm{mV} \\ &= - 1\,\mathrm{V} \end{aligned}$$

So you have an amplifier that multiplies a positive input voltage a hundred times. However, the output voltage will be negative, as pin 3 is being held at 0 volts.

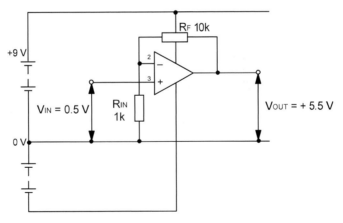

**Figure 1.82** *Non-inverting negative feedback voltage amplifier*

Voltage gain, $A_{\mathrm{Vel}} = + 1\ R_{\mathrm{F}}/R_{\mathrm{IN}}$

$$\begin{aligned} A_{\mathrm{vel}} \ &= V_{\mathrm{out}}/V_{\mathrm{in}} = + 1 + \frac{R_{\mathrm{F}}}{R_{\mathrm{IN}}} \\ &= + 1 + \frac{10\ \mathrm{k}}{1\ \mathrm{k}} \\ &= + 11 \end{aligned}$$

$$V_{\mathrm{out}} = + 11 \times 0.5\,\mathrm{V}$$

$$V_{\mathrm{out}} = + 5.5\,\mathrm{V}$$

Therefore in a circuit where the input voltage is 0.5 V, the output voltage is equal to + 5.5 V. So you have an amplifier that multiplies a positive input voltage eleven times, with a positive output.

### The advantage of negative feedback

As explained, in order to control the gain of an op amp, a feedback resistor must be connected between output at pin 6, $V_{out}$ and the input at pin 2, $V_{IN}$. This is called negative feedback and is useful to control the voltage gain of the op amp from the high open-loop value, $A_{Vol}$, of 100 000 or more, depending on the op amp, to a lower closed-loop gain value $A_{Vel}$ of, say, 100. The effect of this is that the closed-loop gain is solely dependent upon the value of the two resistors $R_{IN}$ and $R_F$. This closed-loop gain is constant irrespective of the type of op amp used or its gain.

## The differential amplifier

It is sometimes useful to use the op amp in the differential mode. A differential amplifier will amplify the difference in voltage between pin 2 and pin 3. The voltage at these pins is referred to as $V_1$ and $V_2$. This is shown in Figure 1.83.

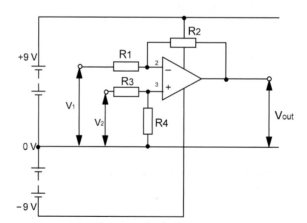

**Figure 1.83** *Difference amplifier*

The differential amplifier will amplify the difference in voltage between $V_1$ and $V_2$ by the gain of the op amp. If this op amp has a gain controlled in a closed-loop system by using a feedback resistor, then $V_{out}$ can be calculated by using the formula:

$$V_{out} = \frac{R_2 (V_2 - V_1)}{R_1}$$

It should be noted that this formula is only correct when $R_4/R_3$ has the same ratio as $R_2/R_1$.

### Summing amplifiers

Operation amplifiers were developed in the 1960s to perform mathematical calculations such as addition. They did this by using analogue signals as the inputs and giving a proportional analogue output. These have largely given way to digital systems but they are still as useful today in situations that require the output voltage to be the sum of the input voltages.

The output voltage of a summing amplifier can be either positive (+) or negative (−) depending upon whether the op amp has its feedback resistors arranged in an inverting or non-inverting mode. In the inverting mode the sum of the voltages will be inverted, that is the output will be negative volts.

### Summing amplifiers explained

If you have two separate input voltages $V_1$ and $V_2$ combining at point X, the voltage at this point will be the sum of the two voltages $V_1$ and $V_2$. This is how it gets the name 'summing amplifier'.

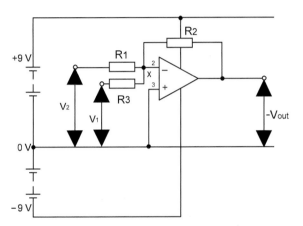

**Figure 1.84** *Summing amplifier*

The gain of a summing amplifier will be, $A_{vel} = -R_F/R_{IN}$ where $R_{IN}$ is the average of the sum of the input resistors.

### Summing amplifiers with the gain equal to unity

When the average of the sum of the input resistors is equal to the value of the feedback resistor, this is called unity gain (one to one). The example shown in Figure 1.85 is a unity gain amplifier where:

$$R_{IN} = \frac{(R_1 + R_3)}{2}$$

$$R_{IN} = \frac{1\,k + 1\,k}{2} = \frac{2\,k}{2}$$

$$R_{IN} = 1\,k$$

Therefore: Voltage gain, $A_{Vel} = -R_F/R_{IN}$
$$A_{vel} = -R_F/R_{IN}$$
$$A_{vel} = -1\,k/1\,k$$
$$A_{vel} = -1$$

**39**

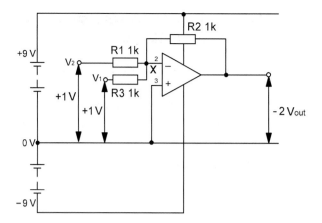

**Figure 1.85** *Summing amplifier with the gain equal to unity*

The voltage out will be the sum of the input voltages multiplied by $R_F / R_{IN}$

For the above example

$$V_{out} = -\frac{R_F}{R_{IN}} \times (V_1 + V_2) = -\frac{1\,k}{1\,k} \times (1V + 1V) = -2V$$

As the output voltage is derived from the inverting pin 2, $V_{out}$ will be a negative voltage i.e., $-2V$.

## Summing amplifiers with the gain greater or less than unity

When a summing amplifier has $R_F$ greater or less than $R_{IN}$ then the voltage gain of the resistor is greater or less than 1. In the example shown in figure 1.85.1 $R_{IN}$ is the average of the sum of the input resistors.

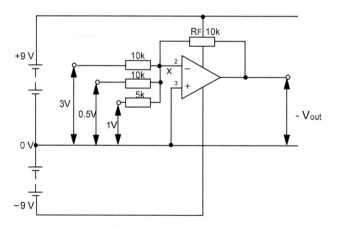

**Figure 1.85.1**
*Summing amplifier with the gain is greater or less than unity*

$R_{IN} = (10\,k + 10\,k + 5\,k)\,/\,3$
$R_{IN} = 8.33\,k$

For this example

$$V_{out} = -\frac{R_F}{R_{IN}} \times (V_1 + V_2 + V_3) = -\frac{10\,k}{8.33\,k} \times (3\,V + 0.5\,V + 1\,V)$$

$V_{out} = -1.2 \times 4.5$

$V_{out} = -5.4\,V$

## Using more than one op amp from a single reference voltage

If more than one op amp is used you can get more than one response to a single variable input signal. The circuit diagram in Figure 1.86 is for a temperature indicator. As the temperature falls below 25°C LEDs start to come on. One LED comes on for every 10°C change in temperature. When the temperature reaches − 5°C, all LEDs will be on.

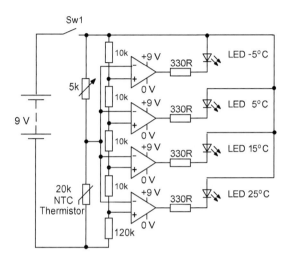

**Figure 1.86** *Quad operational amplifier temperature sensor*

## How it works

Fixed resistors are arranged in series between the positive and negative rails and act as four potential voltage dividers. A connection is made between each pair of resistors and the non-inverting pin of each op amp (pin 3 on the 3140 op amp). Each op amp will now receive a different voltage due the potential difference between each resistor. A second potential divider is made up of a 10 k variable resistor and a 20 k NTC, at 20°C, thyristor. A common output is established between the variable resistor and the thermistor and is connected to all the non-inverting pins of the op amps (pin 2 on the 3140 and 741 op

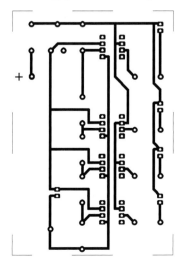

**Figure 1.86.1** *PCB for quad operational amplifier temperature sensor*

amp). As the temperature falls, the voltage between the variable resistor and the thermistor starts to rise. This rise in voltage appears at the non-inverting pins and is compared to the fixed voltage at the inverting pins. When the inverting pin of the op amp is greater than its non-inverting pin, then that op amp is turned off. This enables the current to flow through the LED into the op amp and out to the negative rail causing it to come on. This is repeated until all the outputs of the op amps are turned off and current can flow through all the LEDs, turning them on.

### Operational amplifier

Four 741 op amps were used in the initial circuits. However, these were changed to the CA3140E as the circuit was being used as a comparator. It is also possible to use a quad op amp. This op amp has four comparators contained in a single 14 pin DIL IC. There are a number of these you can purchase. However, the LM319 is a good choice.

### Power supply

A single power supply is required for this circuit as the op amp is being used as a comparator.

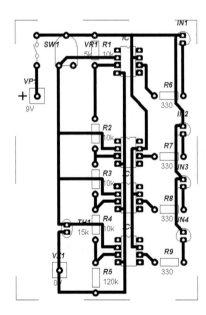

**Figure 1.86.2** Silk screen for quad operational amplifier temperature sensor

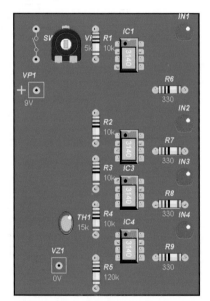

**Figure 1.86.3** Top view of the quad operational amplifier temperature sensor

### Bill of materials

4 × 10 k resistors
1 × 120 k resistor
4 × 330 ohms resistors
1 × 22 k variable resistor
4 × 5 mm red LEDs
1 × 20 k NTC thermistor
4 × 8 pin DIL sockets

4 × CA3140E op amps
1 × SPST miniature toggle switch
1 × 9 volt PP3 battery and clip
1 × board 63.5 mm × 93 mm

# Digital Electronics

The term digital electronics is given to those devices that react to an input signal or turn on an output signal that is in one of two states, on or off. Car lights could be described as digital devices. When you throw the switch, the lights are on. Throw it again and the lights are off. This is different from other electronic devices such as the volume control on your radio. When this is turned the volume will increase or decrease as the voltage is increased or decreased. This is called an analogue signal.

## Digital signals

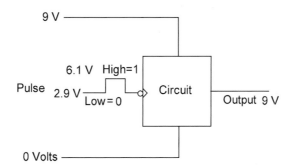

**Figure 1.87** *Pulsing a digital circuit*

In digital electronics a high signal is one that is greater than ⅔ the supply voltage. A low signal is one that is less than ⅓ the supply voltage.

A high signal is represented by a 1.
A low signal is represented by a 0.

In the circuit diagram shown in Figure 1.87, a digital pulse is offered to the circuit to make the output come on. The signal has to go high then low again, to be a pulse.

## Output signals from digital ICs

### Output voltage

The output signal from a digital circuit will be close to the supply voltage. At this level we tend to ignore the small drop in voltage and refer to it as equal to the supply voltage.

### Output current

The output current from digital ICs tends to be very small in relation to supply current. This is due to the internal resistance of the IC. To overcome this it will be necessary to amplify the output

**43**

current. Transistors are commonly used. This is shown in Figure 1.88.

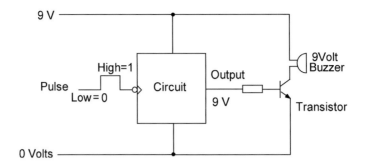

**Figure 1.88** *Amplifying the output signals from ICs*

### Logic gates

Logic gates are digital devices that respond to a digital signal by turning an output on or off. A simple circuit with two switches can be used to make a logic gate. SW1 and SW2 must be pressed to make the lamp come on. This is called an **AND** logic circuit and is shown in Figure 1.89. A simple **OR** logic circuit is shown in Figure 1.90.

The state of the output for both of these simple logic gates can be expressed in a truth table. When the input is high it is shown in the truth table as a 1, with a low as a 0. The resulting output is then shown in the same way, high or low (1 or 0). This is shown in Figures 1.91–2

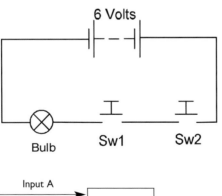

**Figure 1.89** *AND logic circuit*

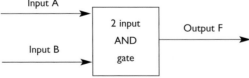

**Table 1** *Truth table for 2 input AND logic circuit*

| Input A | Input B | Output F |
|---------|---------|----------|
| 0 | 0 | 0 |
| 1 | 0 | 0 |
| 0 | 1 | 0 |
| 1 | 1 | 1 |

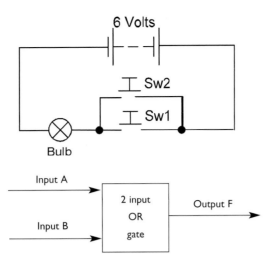

**Figure 1.90** *OR logic circuit*

**Table 2** *Truth table for 2 input OR logic circuit*

| Input A | Input B | Output F |
|---------|---------|----------|
| 0 | 0 | 0 |
| 1 | 0 | 1 |
| 0 | 1 | 1 |
| 1 | 1 | 1 |

### 2 input AND logic gate

The 2 input AND logic circuit will give a high output (logic 1) at F when input A and B are high. If any other combination is present at the gate then the output will be low (logic 0).

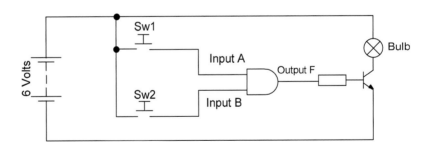

**Figure 1.91** *Circuit diagram for an AND gate*

**Table 3** *Truth table for 2 input AND gate*

| Input A | Input B | Output F |
|---------|---------|----------|
| 0 | 0 | 0 |
| 1 | 0 | 0 |
| 0 | 1 | 0 |
| 1 | 1 | 1 |

**Figure 1.92** *Symbol for the AND gate*

### 2 Input NAND logic gate

The NAND gate is simply the opposite to the AND gate. NAND stands for not AND. For the circuit shown in Figure 1.93, only when both inputs are high (1) will the output at F be off (0). If any other combination is present at the gate then the output at F will be on (1). This is shown in Figure 1.96.

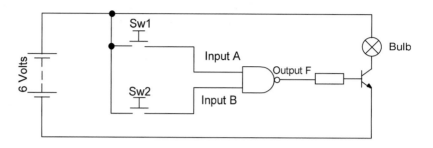

**Figure 1.93** *Circuit diagram for 2 input NAND circuit*

**Table 4** *Truth table for 2 input NAND gate*

| Input A | Input B | Output F |
|---------|---------|----------|
| 0 | 0 | 1 |
| 1 | 0 | 1 |
| 0 | 1 | 1 |
| 1 | 1 | 0 |

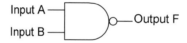

**Figure 1.94** *Symbol for a NAND gate*

### 2 input OR logic gate

The 2 input OR logic circuit will give a high output (logic 1) at F when input A or B are high. Only when both inputs are low will the output will be low (logic 0). This is shown in the truth table.

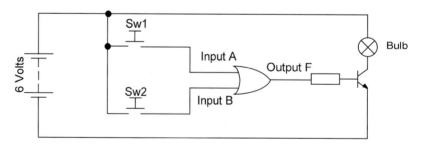

**Figure 1.95** *Circuit diagram for an OR gate*

**Table 5** *Truth table for 2 input OR gate*

| Input A | Input B | Output F |
|---------|---------|----------|
| 0 | 0 | 0 |
| 1 | 0 | 1 |
| 0 | 1 | 1 |
| 1 | 1 | 1 |

**Figure 1.96** *Symbol for the OR gate*

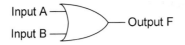

### 2 input NOR logic gate

The NOR gate is simply the opposite to the OR gate. NOR stands for not OR. In this circuit only when both inputs are low (0) will the output be high. If any other combination is present at the gate then the output at F will be low.

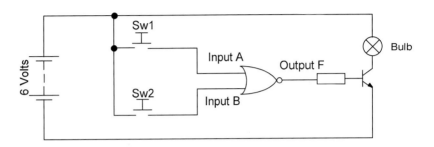

**Figure 1.97** *Circuit diagram for 2 input NOR circuit*

**Table 6** *Truth table for 2 input NOR gate*

| Input A | Input B | Output F |
|---------|---------|----------|
| 0 | 0 | 1 |
| 1 | 0 | 0 |
| 0 | 1 | 0 |
| 1 | 1 | 0 |

**Figure 1.98** *Symbol for the NOR gate*

# Designing circuits using logic gates

Logic gates have been used successfully in electronic circuits for many years now and most of the possible combinations of logic gates have been available in IC packages for almost as long.

The two main families of semiconductor ICs are the 7400 (TTL) and 4000 series (CMOS).

The 7400 series ICs require 5 V +/− 0.1 V, to make them work. The 4000 series ICs require 3–18 V, to make them work.

Both have their advantages and disadvantages. The 4000 series can operate between 3 and 18 V, which makes them very useful for project work. On the other hand, they are sensitive to static.

Static electricity is present in all of us and this can be as high as 2500 volts. How often have you touched someone or got out of a car only to get a small electric shock? This is static electricity

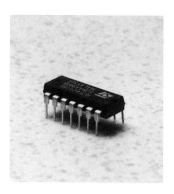

**Figure 1.99** *Picture of
a semiconductor 14 pin IC*

discharging through you to the earth. Fortunately, the current is very small and we suffer no real harm. On the other hand, if you were to touch any of the 4000 series ICs this static charge would damage them. It is good practice to use an anti-static aid while working with CMOS ICs, or at least discharge the static in your body to ground by touching a radiator, or stainless steel sink, before handling these ICs.

If you decide to use the 7400 series ICs you will need to add a 5 V, voltage regulator to your circuit to maintain a constant 5 volts in your circuit.

To standardise the following circuit designs, the **CMOS 4000** series will be used throughout this section of the book.

## Unused outputs

Most of the ICs you will be using contain more than one logic gate. Therefore it is important to tie any unused outputs high or low by connecting them to the positive or negative rails. This will prevent false signals on your IC.

| Example | **Designing a circuit using AND logic** |
|---|---|

The circuit diagram shown in figure 1.102 could be used on a safety guard so that SW1 and SW2 must be closed before the motor will turn.

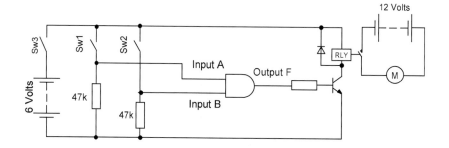

**Figure 1.100** *2 input
AND circuit*

## How it works

SW1 and SW2 are N/O micro-switches. When SW1 and SW2 are closed, a high will be present at both inputs on the gate. Only when this state exists will the output go high. Any other combination will result in a low output. The combinations of inputs and outputs can be seen in the truth table.

The output signal is amplified through the BC108 transistor that turns on the relay. The function of the relay is to switch on the secondary 12 V circuit. This is shown in figure 1.102.

The 4081 IC contains four AND gates arranged head-to-head on the chip. This is called a quad 2 input AND gate. For this circuit you will be using only one gate. Unused gates should have their outputs tied high or low to prevent false signals at other inputs on the IC. The pin layout and truth table for the CMOS4081 IC is shown in Figure 1.103

**Table 7** *Truth table for 2 input AND gate*

| Input A | Input B | Output F |
|---------|---------|----------|
| 0 | 0 | 0 |
| 1 | 0 | 0 |
| 0 | 1 | 0 |
| 1 | 1 | 1 |

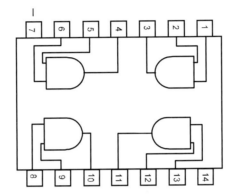

**Figure 1.101** *CMOS 4081 package*

### Circuit diagram for the safety guard using the CMOS4081

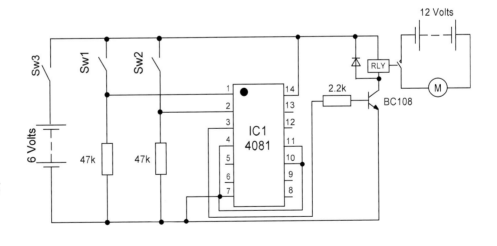

**Figure 1.102** *CMOS 4081 quad 2 input AND gate*

## Building the circuit

When designing a circuit incorporating an IC it is good practice to start by connecting the power supply to the IC. In this case as with many other ICs the top right pin (pin14 in this case) is the positive supply and the bottom left pin (pin 7 in this case) is connected to negative. Next the output can be connected to any one of the 4 AND gates. This circuit uses the top left gate. Pin 3 will be the output. Pins 1 and 2 are the inputs. The inputs are connected to the supply rail through two N/O micro switches SW1 and 2. This is shown in Figure 1.102.

Only when both inputs are high will the output go high. The output signal is connected to a BC108 transistor for current amplification. Only when the output is high will the relay close the secondary contacts causing the motor to turn.

## Author's Notes

Although not necessary, it is good practice to pull the inputs pins high or low through a 47 k resistor rather than leaving them floating. Floating signals can find their way back to other inputs causing a circuit to malfunction. It is good practice to use a relay and secondary circuit as shown in Figure 1.104 if you wish to drive a motor. The problem of false signals generated by motors can be a major problem with logic circuits and can also cause your circuit to malfunction. This can be avoided by isolating your motor through a relay.

### Electromotive devices

The relay used in this circuit is called an electromotive device. This means that it has a copper coil that, when switched on, allows current to flow through it. The coil is wrapped around a soft metal core, which becomes magnetised when current flows in the coil. When you switch off the current, electrons are trapped in the copper coil and soft metal core. To prevent damage to other components in the circuit you will need to use a diode to allow the electrons to return to the battery. This is referred to as back e.m.f (electro-motive-force).

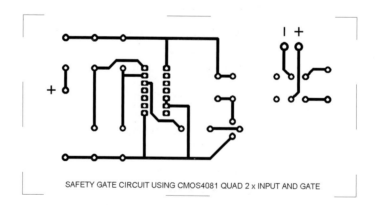

**Figure 1.103** *PCB for the safety gate*

SAFETY GATE CIRCUIT USING CMOS4081 QUAD 2 x INPUT AND GATE

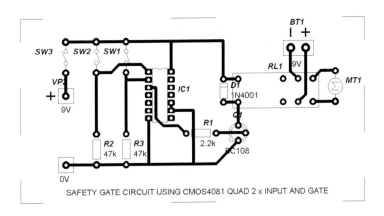

**Figure 1.104** *Silk screen for the safety gate*

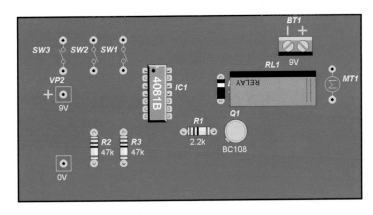

**Figure 1.105** *Top view of the PCB for the safety gate*

### Diodes

Diodes are like one-way valves. They allow electrons to pass easily through them in the direction of the arrow and prevent them from flowing in the other direction. A band, usually silver, will indicate the free flowing direction. This is shown in Figure 1.106.

It is worth noting that diodes have some internal resistance and will cause a voltage drop of 0.7 V in the free flowing direction.

Free flow ➡

**Figure 1.106** *Drawing and symbol for a diode*

### Bill of Materials

1 × 4081 quad 2-Input AND gate IC
2 × micro-switches
1 × SPST toggle switch
1 × 14 pin DIL socket
1 × miniature DPDT relay
1 × BC108 transistor
1 × IN4001 diode
2 × 47 k resistors
1 × 2.2 k resistor
1 × PCB 116.8 mm × 70 mm

| Example | **Designing a circuit using NAND logic** |

#### Situation

A family has a pet cat that likes to go out in the evenings. The cat flap is quite large and if left open could be a security risk. The

**Figure 1.107** *Picture of the inside of the cat flap*

**Figure 1.108** *Picture of the outside of the cat flap*

**Figure 1.109** *Circuit diagram cat flap using a flip flop made from two NAND gates*

problem is that it is difficult to know if the cat is in or out. When the cat is in, the cat flap can be locked from the inside to secure the house.

### Solution

A new cat flap was made to fit into a hole cut in the back door. The front trim, located on the inside, was detachable. This was removed during fitting so that the unit would pass through the hole in the door before being refitted and the unit being secured in place. A bead of mastic was applied to the outside trim to prevent water coming in around the unit.

The cat flap had two LEDs at the top of the inside panel to act as indicators. The flap was hinged at the top so that the cat could push the flap to come in or go out. When the cat went out the red LED came on. When the cat came in the movement of the flap made a green LED come on.

### Circuit diagram for the cat flap

The solution was to use a circuit containing two NAND gates arranged to form an R-S (Rest/Set) flip flop circuit. SW1 and 2 were reed switches attached to the inside and outside top edges of the flap. The final circuit is shown in Figure 1.114.

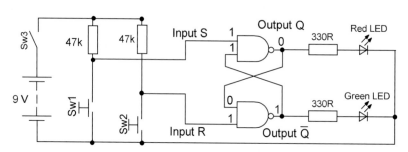

### How it works

Switches 1 and 2 were reed switches fitted to the frame just above the cat flap. A magnet was fixed to the inside and outside of the flap. When the cat pushes the flap open to go out, the magnet moves up to activate the reed switch that in turn triggers the flip flop to bring on output Q (red LED). When the cat returns it pushes open the flap which activates SW2 to bring on output $\bar{Q}$ (green LED).

The 4011 quad 2-input NAND gates can be used to make the flip flop circuit. By connecting the outputs and inputs as shown in Figure 1.109, it is possible to make the R-S flip flop.

The pin layout for the 4011 is shown in Figure 1.110. As this is a quad 2-input NAND gate. You will only need two of the four gates to build this circuit. The unused outputs should be tied high or low to prevent false signals.

**Table 8** *Truth table for 2 input NAND gate*

| Input A | Input B | Output F |
|---------|---------|----------|
| 0 | 0 | I |
| I | 0 | I |
| 0 | I | I |
| I | I | 0 |

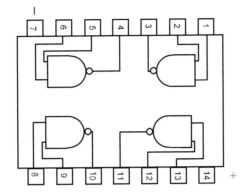

**Figure 1.110**

*CMOS4011 quad 2 input NAND IC*

### Understanding the RS flip flop

When the circuit is switched on the two 47 k resistors keep a **logic 1** at both NAND gates. When **SW1** is pressed a **logic 0** will be present at the top input **S**.

A logic 0 and logic 1 at this gate will give a logic 1 at output Q. The logic 1 at Q sends a logic 1 to the top input at the lower gate R keeping the output off. When the lower gate receives logic 0 by pressing SW2, output Q will go back to logic 0 and $\bar{Q}$ will go to logic 1.

The truth table for the R-S flip flop built from two NAND gates is shown in Table 9.

**Table 9** *Truth table for an R-S flip flop*

| Inputs | | Output | | Comments |
| S | R | Q | $\bar{Q}$ | |
|---|---|---|---|---|
| I | I | NC | NC | No change, latch remains in present state |
| I | 0 | I | 0 | Latch SETS red LED on |
| 0 | I | 0 | I | Latch RESETS green LED on |

The circuit diagram for building an R-S flip flop is shown in Figure 1.111.

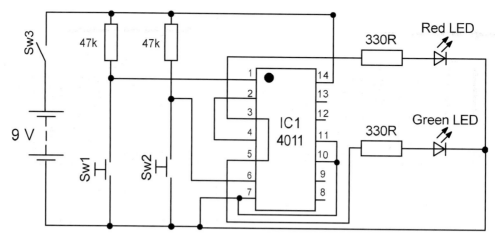

**Figure 1.111** *Circuit diagram for cat flap using a R-S flip flop*

### Author's notes

In the actual circuit, two reed switches were used as the input SW1 and SW2.

Care must be taken when handling the CMOS4011B as all CMOS devices are very sensitive to static electricity. Static electricity is present in your body to a greater or lesser degree depending on the clothes you are wearing. Man-made fibres will produce a lot of static electricity, as much as 2500 volts. If you have ever taken off your man-made jumper or shirt and heard a crackling sound, that is static electricity discharging out off your body. It takes at least 2500 volts to make that sound. While this static electricity is not dangerous to us as the current is very small, it will damage your IC each time you touch it. Eventually it will be damaged beyond repair.

It is important to wear an earth strap connected to a suitably earthed device. If an earth strap is not available, you can discharge the static electricity from your body by touching a metal radiator or steel sink.

### *Bill of materials*

1 × 4011B quad 2 input NAND gate IC
1 × 14 pin DIL socket
1 × PPS3 battery and clip
2 × 47 k resistors
2 × 330 ohms resistors
1 × red LED
1 × green LED
2 × reed switches and magnets
1 × PCB 68 mm × 50 mm

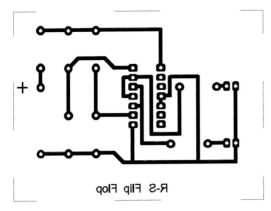

**Figure 1.112** *PCB for cat flap*

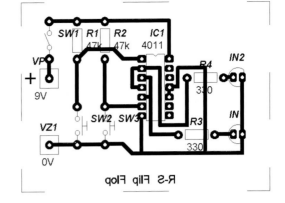

**Figure 1.113** *Silk screen for cat flap*

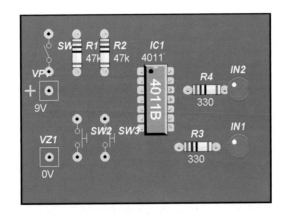

**Figure 1.114** *Top view of PCB for cat flap*

| Example | **Designing a circuit using OR logic** |
|---|---|

### Situation

A cold storage company has a walk-in freezer. The sliding door is opened by an electric motor. To open the door, the forklift truck drives over a push-to-make sensor in the floor. Once in the freezer, the forklift truck drives over another push-to-make sensor, which closes the door. On a number of occasions, staff have walked into the freezer behind the forklift and were unable to open the door.

### Solution

The solution was use an OR gate circuit shown in figure 1.115.

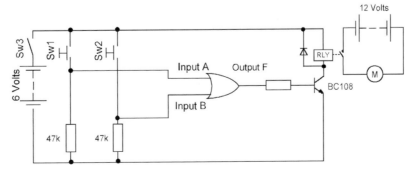

**Figure 1.115** *OR gate operating a freezer door*

**55**

### How it Works

The circuit was designed so that a high input at either SW1 or SW2 would operate the motor. The truth table shows what the output will be depending upon the input. The only time the output is not responding to an input is when both inputs are low.

A CMOS4071 quad 2-input IC was used. The package layout for this is shown in Figure 1.120.

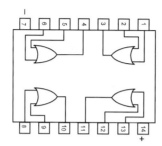

**Figure 1.116**

*CMOS4071 quad 2-input OR IC*

**Table 10** *Truth table for 2 input OR gate*

| Input A | Input B | Output F |
|---------|---------|----------|
| 0 | 0 | 0 |
| 1 | 0 | 1 |
| 0 | 1 | 1 |
| 1 | 1 | 1 |

### Circuit Diagram

The final circuit diagram included limit switches at either end of the track. These stopped the motor even when SW1 and SW2 were still being pressed. This prevented the door from going beyond the limit of the track.

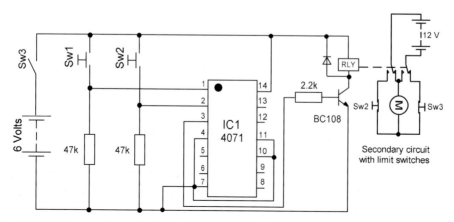

**Figure 1.117** *OR logic circuit for freezer door*

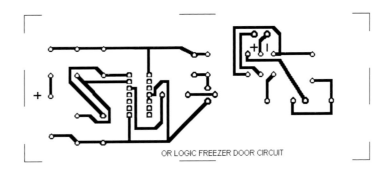

**Figure 1.118** *PCB for freezer door*

OR LOGIC FREEZER DOOR CIRCUIT

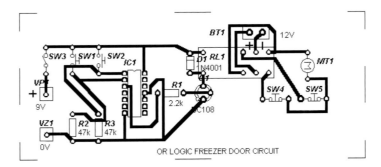

**Figure 1.119** *Silk screen for freezer door*

OR LOGIC FREEZER DOOR CIRCUIT

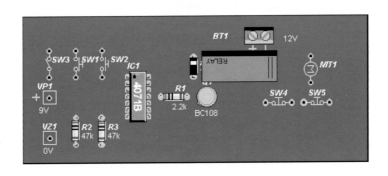

**Figure 1.120** *Top view of the PCB for freezer door*

### Bill of Materials

1 × CMOS4071 quad 2-input OR gate
2 × 47 k resistors
1 × 2.2 k resistor
1 × miniature DPDT relay
1 × IN4001 diode
1 × SPST toggle switch
2 × push-to-break switches
1 × BC108 transistor
1 × PCB 134.6 mm × 56 mm

| Example | **Designing a circuit using NOR logic** |
|---|---|

### Situation

Playing board games that require the quizmaster to accept the first right answer can be difficult to judge. The constant arguments as to who answered first often leads to players or teams giving up before the quiz is over. There is a need for a circuit that will react to a player or team that presses the button first, locking out the opponents.

### Solution

The solution was a double NOR gate circuit. The circuit could identify the first player to press the button. By adding a latch to the output it was possible to lock out the other team. The quizmaster could then reset the circuit for the next question when he/she was ready. The circuit is shown in Figure 1.121.

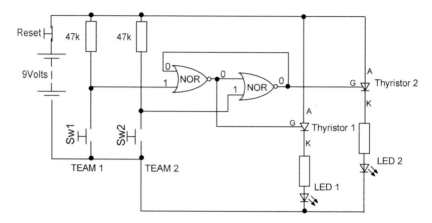

**Figure 1.121** *2-NOR gate quizmaster*

### How it works

Team 1 must press SW1 when they have the correct answer. Team 2 must press SW2.

When SW1 is pressed first then this causes both inputs on gate 1 to go low. As you can see from the truth table two low inputs will make the output go high. A high will cause thyristor 1 to latch on. This in turn will bring on LED 1. The game cannot continue until the quizmaster presses SW3. The same reaction in the circuit will happen to thyristor 2 if SW2 is pressed first.

**Table 11** *Truth table for 2 input NOR gate*

| Input A | Input B | Output F |
|---------|---------|----------|
| 0 | 0 | 1 |
| 1 | 0 | 0 |
| 0 | 1 | 0 |
| 1 | 1 | 0 |

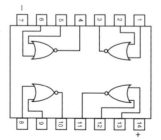

**Figure 1.122**

*CMOS4001 quad 2 input NOR gate IC*

### Circuit Design

The circuit incorporated two gates on a CMOS4001 NOR 2 input IC. The circuit is shown in Figure 1.123.

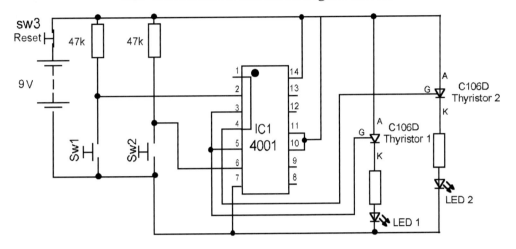

**Figure 1.123** *CMOS4001 Quad 2 input NOR gate quizmaster*

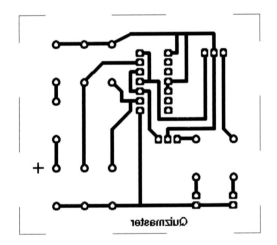

**Figure 1.124** *PCB for quizmaster*

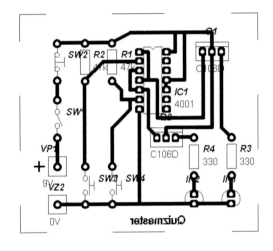

**Figure 1.125** *Silk screen for quizmaster*

### Bill of materials

1 × CMOS4001 quad 2 input NOR IC
1 × 14 pin DIL socket
2 × 330 resistors
2 × 47 k resistors
2 × push-to-make switches
2 × C106D Thyristor
1 × push-to-break switch
1 × SPST miniature toggle switch
1 × yellow LED
1 × red LED
1 × PCB 66 mm × 58 mm

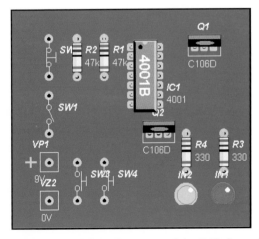

**Figure 1.126** *Top view of the PCB for quizmaster*

# Counting

The ability of a circuit to count pulses is very important in digital electronics. There are a number of different ICs on the market that perform the function of counting. These are referred to as counters and their basic function is to count events. They do this by recognising a pulse (high signal followed by a low signal) and remembering it, before going on to the next operation in the sequence, when another pulse arrives. This storage of information in the ICs memory is important when counting.

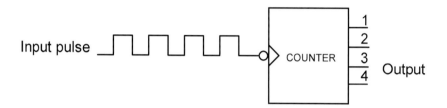

**Figure 1.127** *Counter used to count input pulses*

The counter shown in Figure 1.127 receives a series of input pulses. The first input pulse to arrive at the counter will turn on output 1. The second pulse output 2 and so on. After the fourth pulse the outputs will start again.

One of the most commonly used counting ICs is the CMOS4017 decade counter. This is shown in Figure 1.128.

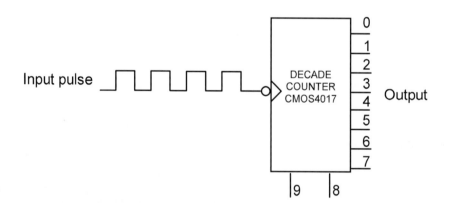

**Figure 1.128**
*CMOS4017 decade counter*

Each time the counter receives a pulse, one of the ten outputs will come on. This happens one after the other, but no more than one output will be on at any one time.

This IC is very useful in situations were you want an output to come on after a set number of pulses. The first pulse would bring on output Q1. If your circuit were designed to come on after 6 pulses you would connect your output device to output number Q6.

## Building a circuit incorporating a decade counter

The CMOS4017 decade counter is a 16 pin DIL IC. Like all ICs it will require a positive and negative power supply to make it function. It has ten outputs numbered Q0-Q9. The pulse is connected to the clock pulse pin 14 labelled CLK. The reset pin 15 is labelled R and is held low through a 47 k resistor. A push-to-make switch allows you to send a high signal to pin 15 to reset the chip at any point in the cycle. The enable pin is pin 13 and is labelled EN, this must be connected to negative through a 47 k resistor for the circuit to operate.

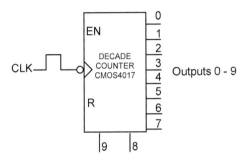

**Figure 1.129** *4017 decade counter*

## Designing a one-hour timing circuit using the CMOS4017 IC

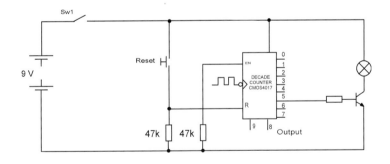

**Figure 1.130** *Circuit diagram for the decade counter*

If the clock pulses are set up to arrive once every twelve minutes, then five pulses would equal one hour. The output connected to output 5 is shown in Figure 1.130. As the pulses are twelve minutes apart, each output would stay on for this length of time, before turning off. To reset the counter to zero you would press the reset switch. To enable the IC to count, the enable pin (EN) must be connected to the negative rail (pulled low) through a 47 k resistor.

### Clock pulse

It is common for the clock pulse to come from a 555 astable timing circuit. The output from pin 3 on the 555 timer is connected to the CLK (clock) pin 14 on the counter. The circuit diagram is shown in Figure 1.132.

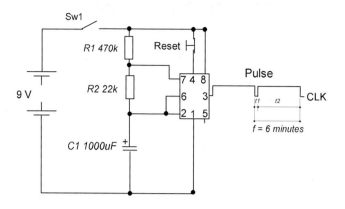

**Figure 1.131** *555 timer used to pulse the counter*

### Calculating the frequency of 555

$t2 = 0.7 \times (R1 + R2) \times C$

$t1 = 0.7 \times R2 \times C1$

$f = t1 + t2$

$t2 = 0.7 \times (470\,000 + 22000) \times 0.001$

$t1 = 0.7 \times 22000 \times 0.001$

$f = 344.4 + 15.4$

$f = 359.8$ seconds

$f = 5.996$ minutes

$f = 6$ minutes (allowing for tolerances)

## Adding the clock pulse to the counter

The clock pulse from the 555 timer circuit is connected to the CLK pin 14 on the counter. It is these pulses that enable the counter to move from one output to the next, in sequence.

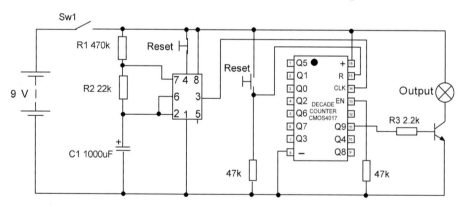

**Figure 1.132** *One-hour timer circuit*

## How it works

The 555 timer sends a clock pulse once every six minutes to the counter. The pulse enables the counter to move on to the next output making it go high in the process. At the tenth pulse, output Q9 will go high, turning on the transistor and lamp. The output will remain on for one time period of 6 minutes before turning off. The counter then moves on to output Q0. This is shown in Figure 1.132.

## CMOS4017 pin layout

The output pins on the 4017 are pins 1–7 and 9–11. Pin 16 is the positive supply, pin 8 the negative, pin 15 is the reset and this must be held low for the IC to work. The clock pulse is connected to pin 14. The enable is pin 13 and must be held low (connected to negative via a 47 k resistor) for the circuit to run. Pin 12 is the carryout pin and can be used to send a pulse to another 4017 after the tenth pulse. The output pins are labelled Q0 – Q9.

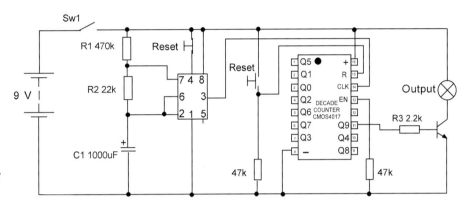

**Figure 1.133** *Circuit diagram for the CMOS4017 decade counter*

## CMOS4017 ten-hour timer

The circuit shown in Figure 1.133 was a one-hour timer. A short pulse happened once every 6 minutes. After ten pulses (one hour) output 9 came on. If a second 4017 has its clock pin connected to the last output or the carryout of the first 4017, a pulse will be detected once every hour. It is possible to connect an output device to any of the ten outputs on IC2. If output Q9 is used as shown in Figure 1.134 it will take ten one-hour pulses before it comes on. By doing this you will have a time delay of 10 hours before the final output at IC2 comes on. A ten-hour time delay circuit using a 555 timer and two decade counters is shown in Figure 1.139.

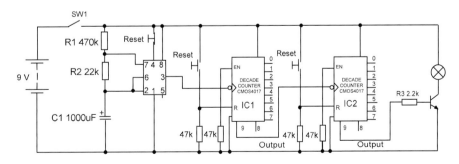

**Figure 1.134** *Ten-hour time delay circuit*

## Six-hour timer

It is possible to stop the count at any time in the cycle by connecting the desired output to the reset. This will send the count back to the start. If you require a circuit that turns on a lamp after 5 hours and stays on for one hour before resetting, this can be achieved using two 4017 decade counters with the sixth output on IC2 connected to the reset. This is shown in Figure 1.135.

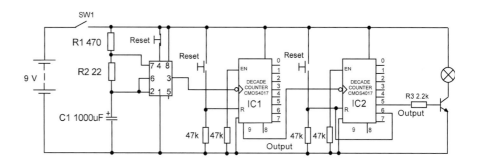

**Figure 1.135** *Six-hour timer circuit*

## 10 LED bar graph display

The 4017 is very useful if you require a number of LEDs to come on one after the other. The example shown in Figure 1.136 will turn on a single LED in sequence. The output display can be purchased, housed in a single package called a bar graph display.

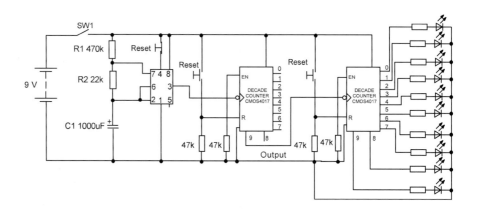

**Figure 1.136** *Bar graph display*

Example

## Electronic rabbit food dispenser

### Design situation

A pet rabbit has to be fed a small amount of food every 12 hours. Some days there is no one in the house from early morning to late evening. On these days there is no one to feed the rabbit. There is a need for an automatic rabbit food dispenser that will come on every 12 hours.

### Solution

The final solution was an electronic device that came on every 12 hours. Rabbit food was placed in the container on the side of the device. When the 12 hours had elapsed, a small motor was turned on. As it rotated, food was emptied out into the rabbit's cage. The device that was fixed to the side of the cage is shown in Figure 1.137.

The knob on the front was connected to a variable resistor and controlled the length of time the motor was on. This was component VR4 in Figure 1.138.

**Figure 1.137** *Picture of 12-hour rabbit feeder*

### Circuit diagram

A 9 V battery powered the circuit. The timing part of the circuit was a 555 astable timer that sent a pulse to the first 4017 decade counter every 8 minutes. This in turn pulsed the second 4017 decade counter after 80 minutes. After a nine pulses to the second 4017 decade counter, the output relay came on. This in turn controlled the 3 V gearbox motor. The length of time for which the relay was on was determined by the value of $VR_4$ and $C_2$. These two components were connected in parallel to the relay. $C_2$ started to charge up when current flowing to the output transistor BC108 was also allowed to flow down through $VR_4$. When $C_2$ was charged it gave a high at the reset pin that caused the second 4017decade counter to reset to Q0. At this moment the output turned off. In the final circuit $R_2$ was changed for a variable resistor so that the length of time for which the motor was on could be controlled more precisely.

## Twelve-hour horse feeder

The technique of using a time delay to reset a 4017 decade counter is fine for short time periods of a few seconds. Longer time-on periods, such as was necessary for the horse feeder shown in Figure 1.139, would require a final output stage that included a 555 monostable circuit, as the hopper had an auger inside that had to be turned on for 4 minutes in order to dispense enough food to the horse.

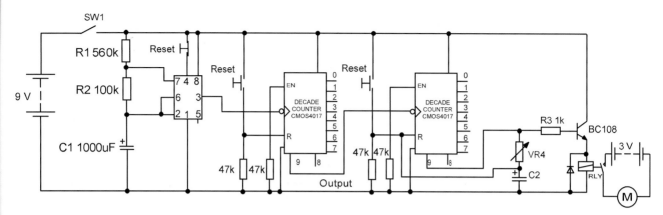

**Figure 1.138** *Circuit diagram for a 12-hour feeder*

**Figure 1.139** *Picture of 12-hour horse feeder*

## Seven-segment LED displays

Seven-segment LED displays are used to display the numbers 0–9. Each segment is a rectangular LED. By arranging the LEDs in this way they can be turned on in specific patterns to illuminate selected numbers.

There is a range of different sizes and colours available but they all work in the same way. That is, by applying a small current to each LED to turn it on. Once you know which LED is connected to which segment, then you can work out which of these you need to turn on to make a specific number.

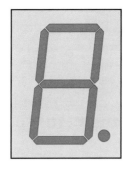

**Figure 1.140** *Seven-segment LED display*

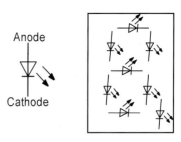

**Figure 1.141** *Eight LEDs forming the seven-segment display*

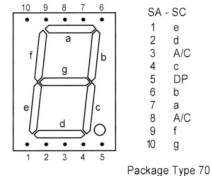

| SA - SC | |
| --- | --- |
| 1 | e |
| 2 | d |
| 3 | A/C |
| 4 | c |
| 5 | DP |
| 6 | b |
| 7 | a |
| 8 | A/C |
| 9 | f |
| 10 | g |

Package Type 70

**Figure 1.142** *Pin identification*

## Connecting the LEDs

The seven-segment displays consist of eight LEDs housed in a plastic package.

There are a number of different packages to suit different sizes of display. The package shown in Figure 1.140 and Figure 1.142 are housed in package 70.

Each LED terminates at a pin on the back of the display. Each pin is numbered so that you know which LED you are turning on. The segments associated with these pins are labelled a–g. The table in Figure 1.142 shows the pin number and the corresponding segment's letter.

All the LEDs in the display will have either a common anode or cathode. SA represents a common anode and SC a common cathode. The arrangement for a common cathode is shown in Figure 1.143.

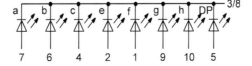

**Figure 1.143** *Common cathode LEDs*

## Using an IC to drive a seven-segment display

There are a number of ICs specially designed to operate seven-segment displays. One of the most popular is the CMOS4026 decade/decoder seven-segment display. When a single pulse is offered to pin 1 on this IC it will turn on the correct output segments to form the number zero. A second pulse will display the number one and so on until number nine is displayed. After nine the display goes back to zero and starts again.

## Getting to know the CMOS4026 IC

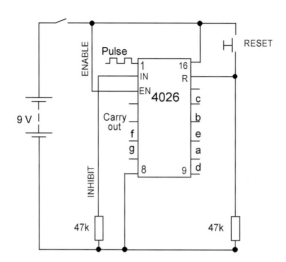

**Figure 1.144** *Pin layout for the 4026 decade/decoder*

Pin 1: Input pin When a pulse is offered to this pin the sequence of outputs to the seven-segment display will change to the next number.

Pin 2: Inhibit A low at this pin will keep the 4026 running.

Pin 3: Enable A high will enable the input to be detected and provided that the inhibit is pulled low, the outputs will keep moving through the sequence.

Pin 4: N/C Not connected

Pin 5: Carry out This pin is used when you wish to count to 99. The function of this pin is to provide a pulse to pin 1 of a second 4026. This pin provides an output to the second 4026 once every tenth pulse.

Pin 8: Negative

Pin 15: Reset This pin must be pulled low through a 47 k resistor. A high at this pin will reset the count to zero.

Pin 16: Positive 3 – 15 V

Output Pins: (6 = f), (7 = g), (9 = d), (10 = a), (11 = e), (12 = b), (13 = c).

## 1 Digit 0–9 counter

Connecting a seven-segment LED display to the 4026 decade/decoder is a simple matter of linking the pins a–g on the IC to the appropriate a–g pins on the display. An example of this using a common cathode seven-segment display package 70 is shown in Figure 1.145.

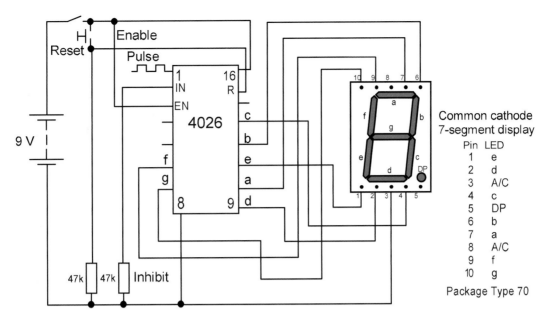

**Figure 1.145** *1-digit 0–9 counter*

## 2 digit 0–99 counter

By using the carry out function on the first 4026 (IC1) that counts the units, it is possible to count from 0 to 99. The carry out goes high once every tenth pulse on IC1. This will be the first pulse offered to the 4026 (IC2) that counts the number of tens. The circuit for this is shown in Figure 1.146.

## Pulsing a CMOS4026 single digit display

Pulsing a 4026 IC is best done through a compatible IC. One of the most commonly used ICs is the 555-astable timer shown in Figure 1.147. Each pulse from the 555 astable will cause the display to count up one digit.

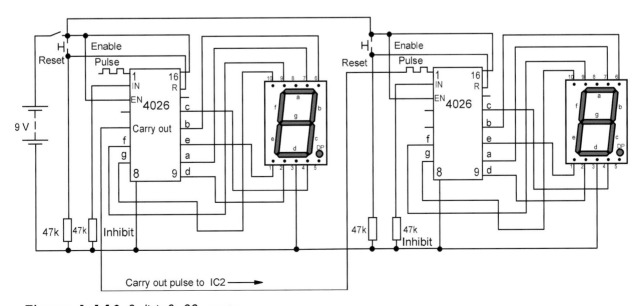

**Figure 1.146** *2 digit 0–99 counter*

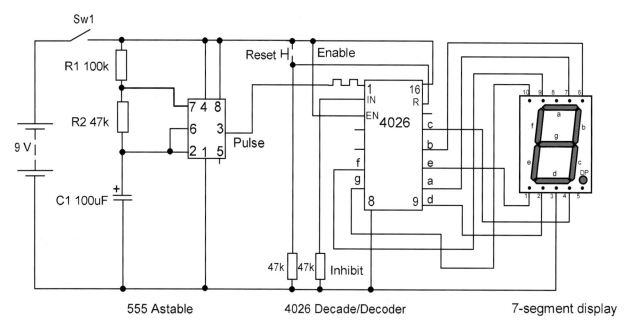

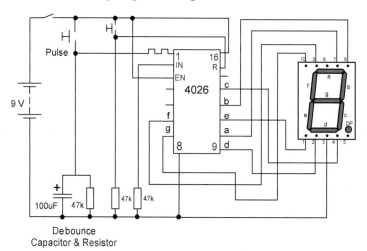

**Figure 1.147** *555 astable – 4026 decade/decoder seven-segment LED display*

### Debouncing a CMOS4026 IC

A problem you are likely to encounter if you use a mechanical switch to pulse your counter will be *bounce*. This is the term given to false signals generated by mechanical switches. This is due to arcing across the contacts of the switch as they pull apart. The effect of this will be more than one pulse and subsequent unwanted counting appearing on your display, even though you have only pressed the switch once. A simple and sometimes effective way to cure this is to add a resistor and capacitor to the input. These should be connected between the push-to-make switch and the negative rail. This is shown in Figure 1.148. If this fails you will need to build a 'Schmitt trigger' and add it to your circuit at the input pulse stage.

**Figure 1.148** *Using a capacitor and resistor input switch to debounce the signal*

### Debounce using Schmitt Trigger

The best method of debouncing your circuit when you are using a mechanical switch is to incorporate a CMOS 40106B Schmitt trigger IC. You will need to add a 100 k resistor and 220 nF capacitor to the input part of the IC. This is shown in Figure 1.149. The circuit has an LED added. The LED is simply there to let you see when the output is high if you wish you might leave it out when incorporating the Schmitt trigger into your circuit designs. The CMOS 40106B has six Schmitt triggers but the circuit shown in Figure 1.152 uses only one of these so you can leave the others unused.

## How it works

The Schmitt trigger is used to obtain a square waveform with a shape rising and falling edge. The capacitor masks the effect of any bouncing at the switch contacts. As soon as the switch is pressed $V_{out}$ rises sharply from 0 V to 9 V and stays there. When the switch is released there is a delay in milliseconds, determined by the value of $R1 \times C1$, before $V_{out}$ drops back to 0 V giving you a single-shape pulse out of the Schmitt trigger. This is shown in Figure 1.150.

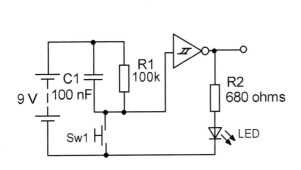

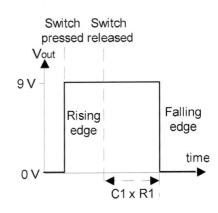

**Figure 1.149** *CMOS 40106B Schmitt trigger circuit*

**Figure 1.150** *Schmitt trigger waveform*

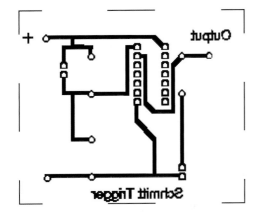

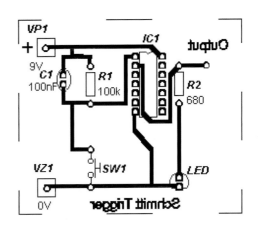

**Figure 1.151** *PCB Schmitt Trigger circuit*

**Figure 1.152** *Silk screen Schmitt Trigger*

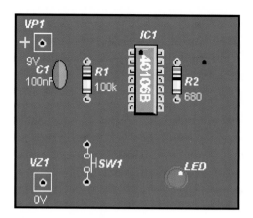

**Figure 1.153** *Top view of the PCB Schmitt Trigger*

## Bill of materials

1 × red LED
1 × 680R resistor
1 × 100 nF polyester capacitor
1 × 100 k resistor
1 × CMOS 40106B Hex Schmitt Trigger IC
1 × board 63 mm × 53 mm

---

**Example**          ## Conveyor 2-digit box counter

### Design situation

A company making shoes needs to detect every hundredth box coming down a conveyor belt. The conveyor belt is then stopped to allow the staff to finish lifting the boxes and to allow them time to package these into a larger transporting box. The problem is to know when one hundred boxes are on the belt and then to stop it moving.

### Solution

The final solution was a 2-digit counter that displayed the numbers 0–99. This enabled the staff to see how many boxes had gone down the conveyor belt. At the end of the count an alarm was sounded to tell the staff to stop the conveyor belt. The sensor to detect each box was a micro-switch fixed to the side of the conveyor. Each box would activate the switch, advancing the count on the display by one. The unit was fixed to the metal conveyor side panel by means of a magnet strip. A drawing of the unit is shown in Figure 1.155.

### Circuit diagram for the 2-digit box counter

The final circuit used a micro-switch to detect the boxes. The signal from the input switch was passed through a Schmitt Trigger to debounce it. This gave a clean pulse to the first 4026 decade/decoder that counted and displayed the units 0–9. On the tenth pulse, a carryout pulse was sent the second 4026 decade/decoder that counted and displayed the tens 10–99. At the

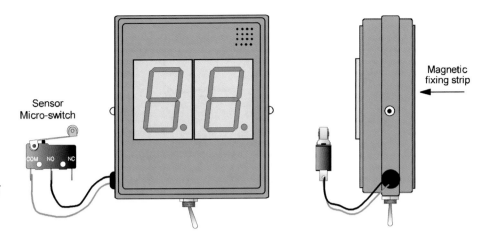

**Figure 1.154** *Drawing of the 2-digit box counter unit*

same time the first 4026 decade/decoder reset its display to zero, ready for the next pulse. The displayed numbers were arranged in the final project with the unit display (0–9) to the right and the tens displayed on the left. The output display was a 40 mm common cathode (negative) seven-segment display. It was found that displays larger than 40 mm required more current than the 4026 decade/decoder could provide and the output had to pass through a Darlington Driver IC to amplify the current.

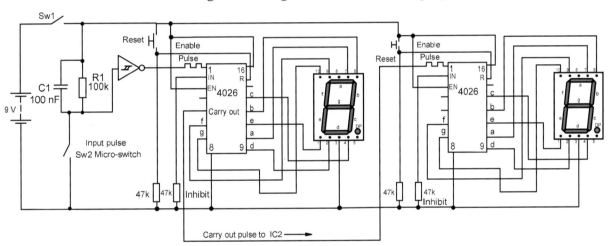

**Figure 1.155** *Circuit diagram for the 2-digit box counter unit*

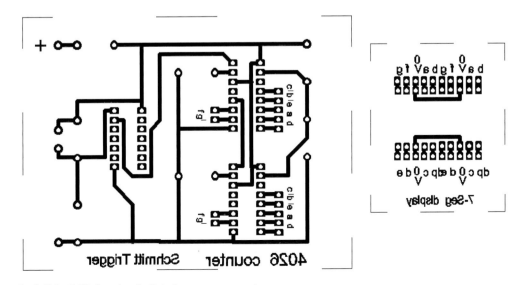

**Figure 1.156** *PCB for the 2-digit box counter unit*

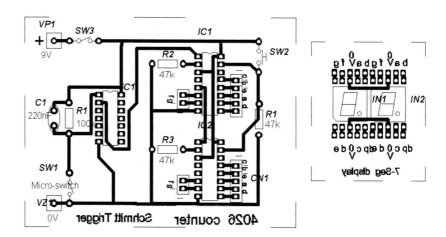

**Figure 1.157** *Silk screen for the 2-digit box counter unit*

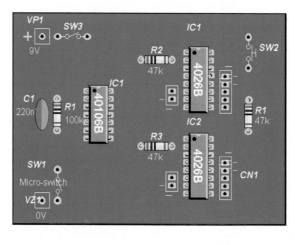

**Figure 1.158** *Top view of the PCB for the 2-digit box counter unit*

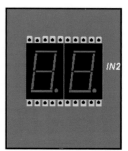

### Bill of materials

1 × 100 k resistor
3 × 47 k resistors
2 × 16 pin DIL sockets
1 × 14 pin DIL socket
2 × 4026B decade/decoders
1 × 40106B Schmitt Trigger IC
2 × seven-segment displays 70 package
1 × 220 µF capacitor
1 × micro-switch
1 × push-to-make switch
1 × miniature toggle switch
1 × PCB 91.4 mm × 68.6 mm
1 × PCB 38 mm × 45.7 mm

## Alternative use for the 2-digit counter unit: golf practice chipping net

The same circuit was the solution to a golf training aid. The project used a micro-switch fixed inside an ejection tube. As the golf balls rolled down the tube they pulsed the circuit. The display indicated the number of balls the player had managed to chip into the net. The picture of the project is shown in Figure 1.159.

**Figure 1.159** *Golf practice chipping net*

# CHAPTER TWO

**Higher Mechanisms**

# Motion

### Types of motion

There are four basic types of motion:

- linear motion
- rotary motion
- reciprocating motion
- oscillating motion.

**Figure 2.1** *Digger in linear motion*

**Figure 2.2** *Pen moving in linear motion*

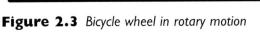

**Figure 2.3** *Bicycle wheel in rotary motion*

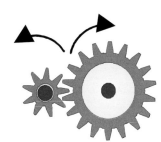

**Figure 2.4** *Spur gears in rotary motion*

### *Linear motion*

Linear means in a straight line, so linear motion is movement in a straight line.

In Figure 2.1 the digger's front bucket is in linear motion as it pushes the soil along the ground. When you rule a line on your page, the pen is moving in linear motion. This is shown in Figure 2.2.

### *Rotary motion*

This is the most common type of motion found in machines.

**75**

Gears, pulleys, wheels, CD players, all turn in rotary motion. Rotary machines can be described as those having mechanisms that go round and round. The bicycle shown in Figure 2.3 is a machine that has wheels that go round and round in rotary motion.

Gears are designed to rotate and transfer rotary motion from one shaft to another. This is shown in Figure 2.4.

### Reciprocating motion

If a mechanism is moving in reciprocating motion this means it is going backwards and forwards or up and down in a straight line. The needle in a sewing machine moves up and down in a straight line as it stitches the cloth. The piston in a car goes up and down in reciprocating motion. The blade in a scroll saw moves up and down in reciprocating motion as it cuts the timber. This is shown in Figure 2.5.

**Figure 2.5** *Scroll saw*

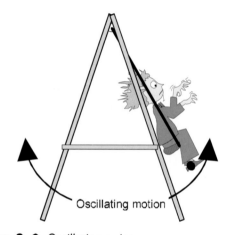

**Figure 2.6** *Oscillating swing*

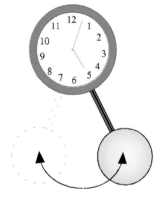

**Figure 2.7** *Oscillating pendulum*

### Oscillating motion

Oscillating means swinging backwards and forwards in an arc shape. Machines that have mechanisms moving in this way are said to be moving in oscillating motion.

When a child is swinging he/she is oscillating. This is shown in Figure 2.6.

The pendulum of the clock shown in Figure 2.7 swings backwards and forwards in an oscillating motion.

# Levers

## Velocity ratio

Is the ratio of movement between the load and effort. The amount of increase or decrease in movement of the lever is called the velocity ratio.

$$VR = \frac{\text{distance moved by effort}}{\text{distance moved by load}}$$

The screwdriver shown in Figure 2.9 was used to lift the lid of the tin. It had to move 2.5 mm to release the lid. The effort at the handle had to move 60 mm to achieve this. The velocity ratio in this case was 24:1.

$$VR = \frac{\text{distance moved by effort}}{\text{distance moved by load}}$$

$$VR = \frac{60}{2.5} = 24 \text{ to } 1 = 24:1$$

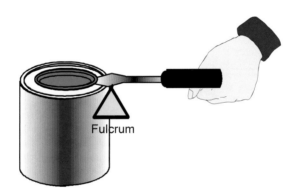

**Figure 2.8** *Releasing the paint tin lid*

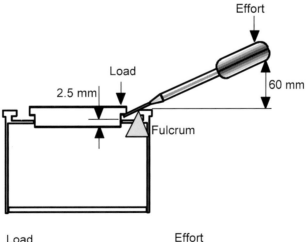

**Figure 2.9** *Sectional view of the paint tin*

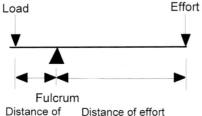

**Figure 2.10** *Mechanical advantage*

## Mechanical advantage

The lever used to open the tin in Figure 2.8 is a class 1 lever. The lever makes it easier for you to open the tin. This lever is said to have a mechanical advantage (MA). This is shown in Figure 2.10.

$$MA = \frac{load}{effort}$$

Also

$$MA = \frac{distance\ of\ effort\ from\ fulcrum}{distance\ of\ load\ from\ fulcrum}$$

**Example**       **Load = ? Effort = 2 kg**

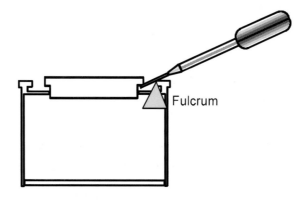

**Figure 2.11** *Mechanical advantage*

In Figure 2.11, an effort of 2 kg is applied to the screwdriver handle. What load will be applied to the tip of the screwdriver to open the tin?

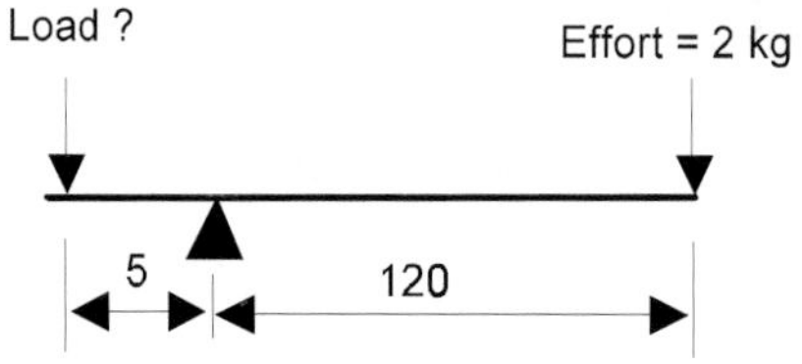

**Figure 2.12** *Mechanical advantage 24:1*

$$MA = \frac{load}{effort}$$

$$load = MA \times effort$$

$$MA = \frac{distance\ of\ effort\ from\ fulcrum}{distance\ of\ load\ from\ fulcrum}$$

$$MA = \frac{120}{5} = 24{:}1$$

Therefore: load = 24 × 2 = 48 kg

Note: kg is a measurement of mass and while this method of calculating the load may be easier to understand (a bag of sugar = 1 kg) the correct units to use are units of force measured in Newtons (1 kg = 10 Newton).

# Moments of force

A moment of force is the tendency for a lever to produce movement around a point. A moment is calculated by **force × distance.** This is shown in Figure 2.13.

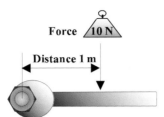

**Figure 2.13** *Moment of force = 10Nm*

The spanner in Figure 2.13 has a force applied 1 m from the turning point of the nut. The moment of force is calculated as follows:

moment = force × distance
moment = 10 × 1
moment = 10 Nm

If you double the distance, the moment of force will double. Figure 2.14 has the force 2 m from the turning point.

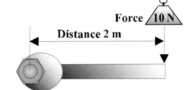

**Figure 2.14** *Moment of force = 20 Nm*

moment: F × D = 10N × 2 m = 20 Nm

# Types of levers

Most levers will be straight. The spanner shown in Figure 2.14 is a straight lever. Not all levers are straight. The lever shown in Figure 2.15 is a bell crank lever.

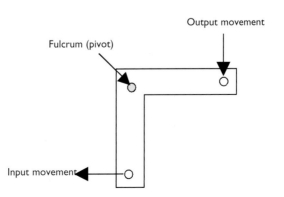

**Figure 2.15** *Bell crank lever*

### Bell crank levers

This is a type of lever bent at right angles. It can be used to change the direction of movement through 90° as shown in Figure 2.16. The upward pulling action of the break cable results in a sideways action of the break rubber against the rim of the wheel.

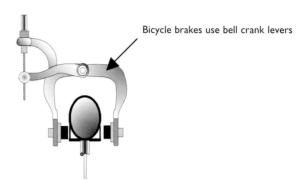

Bicycle brakes use bell crank levers

**Figure 2.16** *Bell crank lever used on bicycle breaks*

### Double bell crank levers

The double bell crank can be used when one input movement results in two output movements. The output movement will be in the opposite direction. A double bell crank lever is shown in Figure 2.17.

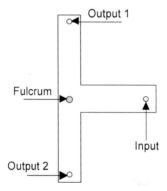

**Figure 2.17** *Double bell crank lever*

### Cam lift

Cam lift is the distance a follower will rise and fall during one complete cycle of the cam this is also known as the stroke. This is shown in Figure 2.18.

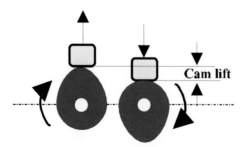

**Figure 2.18** *Cam lift*

### Friction

One of the major problems with cams is friction between the cam and the follower and at the sides of the follower in the guides as shown in Figure 2.19.

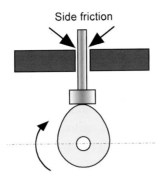

**Figure 2.19** *Follower friction*

Friction can be reduced in a number of ways, such as making the cam lift as small as is practical or by fixing a small roller bearing on the end of the follower, to reduce friction between the end of the follower and the edge of the cam.

Side friction and wear can be reduced using hardened metal guides. Alternatively, on small projects, nylon tubing will make a good guide and considerably reduce friction.

Oil is also used to reduce friction between the follower and its guide and also between the cam and follower.

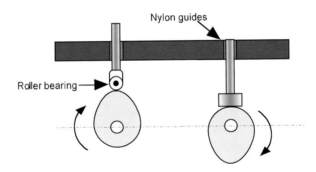

**Figure 2.20** *Nylon guides to reduce friction*

## Flat linear plate cams

The cams shown in Figures 2.18–20 are of the circular plate type. These rotate and are in rotary motion about the axis. Not all cams rotate, some slide and are called 'flat linear plates cams'.

A flat linear plate cam is shown in Figure 2.21. The profile of the flat linear plate cam will be designed to create the desired rise and fall in the follower.

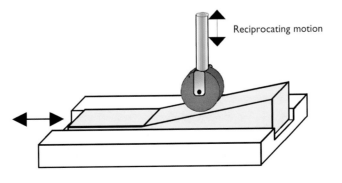

**Figure 2.21** *Flat linear plate cam*

## Profile of linear flat plate cams

A follower, capable of rising and falling with uniform velocity due to the profile of the plate, is shown in Figure 2.21. The motion of the flat linear plate cam creates reciprocation motion in the follower.

The profile of the flat plate cam shown in Figure 2.22 will create a sudden rise and fall in the follower when the follower reaches the convex part of the plate. This is similar to the motion of the pear-shaped cam.

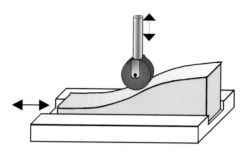

**Figure 2.22** *Flat linear plate cam*

## Cam motion

Circular plate cams rotate. This motion is converted into reciprocating output motion within the follower. These cams normally rotate with a constant velocity of rotation. Parts of a cam are shown in Figure 2.23.

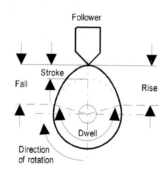

**Figure 2.23** *Parts of a cam*

### Follower displacement

You can plot the path of the rise and fall of your cam as it moves through 360° by dividing the profile of the cam into equal parts, lifting the length from the centre to the edge and plotting these lengths onto the graph as shown in Figures 2.24 and 2.25.

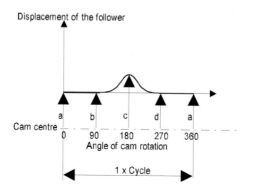

**Figure 2.25** *Plotting the displacement of the cam and follower*

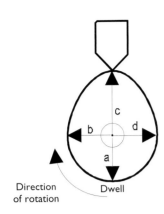

**Figure 2.24** *Dividing the profile of the cam into equal parts*

### Plotting the profile of a cam by angular rotation

It is possible to plot the displacement of a cam geometrically. The cam shown in Figure 2.26 has its rotation divided into equal units each representing 45°.

- To plot the displacement a compass is placed on the centre axis of the cam and is used to pick up the points that intersect the 45° lines.
- The points are then projected round to meet the vertical line at 0°.
- These points are then projected horizontally across to intersect equally spaced vertical displacement lines on the displacement diagram.
- The points of intersection are then plotted to give the displacement of the follower as the cam rotates clockwise.
- The eccentric cam shown in Figure 2.26 is a circular flat plate cam that will produce a simple harmonic motion in the follower.

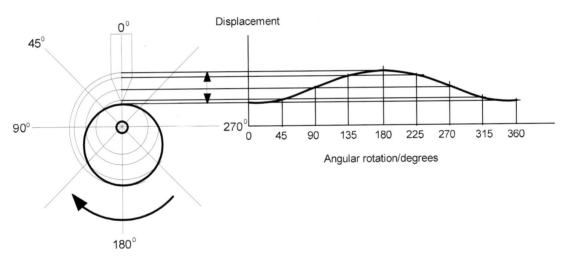

**Figure 2.26** *Displacement diagram for an eccentric cam*

### Follower motion
#### Reciprocating motion

The most common type of motion of the follower is reciprocating motion. This is shown in Figure 2.27, where the rotary motion of the circular plate cam is producing reciprocating motion in the flat follower.

#### Oscillating motion

It is also possible to make the follower move with oscillating motion as shown in Figure 2.28.

**Figure 2.27** *Flat follower moving up and down in reciprocating motion*

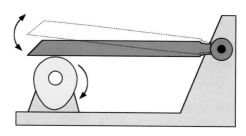

**Figure 2.28** *Follower in oscillating motion*

### Keeping the follower in contact with the cam

In simple projects the follower's own weight can be used to hold it against the cam.

For precise movement of the follower, a spring is used to keep the follower in contact with the cam at all times.

A compression spring is used to hold the follower in contact with the pear-shaped plate cam. This is shown in Figure 2.29.

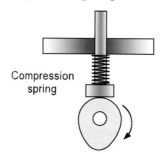

Compression spring

**Figure 2.29**
*Compression spring*

A tension spring can also be used to keep the follower in contact with the cam. An example of this is shown in Figure 2.30.

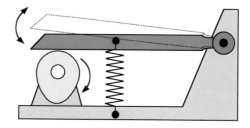

**Figure 2.30** *Tension spring*

## Introduction to linkages

A linkage is a rigid bar or rod used to transmit movement. Linkages are used in many every day products like a bicycle chain. As shown in Figure 2.31

The chain enables the cyclist to transmit motion, from the front pedals to the rear wheel.

**Figure 2.31** *Bicycle chain*

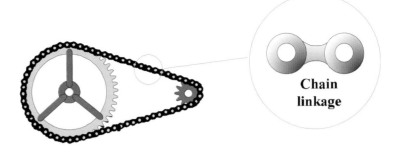

**Figure 2.32** *Lots of linkages are used to make a bicycle chain*

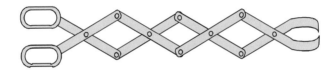

**Waste material lifting device**

### Design situation

There is a need for a grab and lifting device that will be used to pick up waste materials.

### Solution

The final solution was a pair of lazy-tongs shown in Figure 2.33. This is a series of linkages that pivot in the middle and at the ends.

**Figure 2.33** *Lazy-tongs using linkages*

## How it works

The waste material placed between the jaws and the handles are forced together. The pressure asserted by the handle is transferred to the ends, enabling the waste material to be lifted.

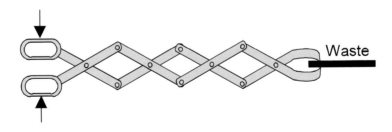

Waste

**Figure 2.34** *Lazy-tongs*

## Linkages used in technology projects

Knowledge of linkages can be helpful in the design and manufacture of technology products. The pictures show examples of how linkages were used in technology products.

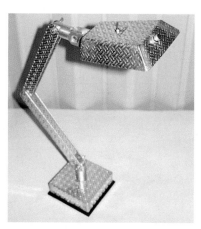

**Figure 2.35** *An adjustable reading light*

**Figure 2.36** *A concrete block lifter*

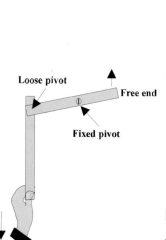

**Figure 2.37** *A bike stand*

## Parts of a linkage

Two or more linkages may be joined together by means of a loose pivot. When the input linkage has to change the direction of the output linkage, then a fixed pivot is added. This is shown in Figure 2.38.

## Types of linkages

There are a number of different types of linkage you can use in your products. Each creates a different movement. In Figure 2.38, an input movement downwards produces an output movement upwards. The distance the free end moves is the same as the loose pivot end held in the hand. This is due to the pivot being in the middle of the linkage.

Figure 2.39 shows how you can make the free end (output) move a greater distance than the loose pivot end (input). This is possible due to the small input movement which results in a large output movement.

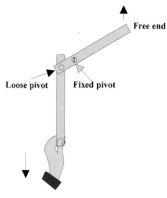

**Figure 2.39** *Small input – Large output*

## Reverse motion linkage

It is possible to change direction using a linkage. The reverse motion linkage shown in Figure 2.40 changes a pulling force into a pushing force by means of a reverse motion linkage.

**Figure 2.38** *Parts of a linkage*

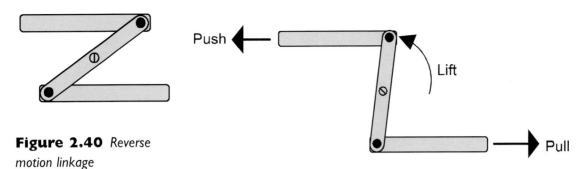

**Figure 2.40** *Reverse motion linkage*

## Linkages in technology products

By connecting levers and linkages together you can design useful technology products.

### Pedal bin

The domestic pedal bin uses linkages to make the lid open.

**Figure 2.41** *Picture of pedal bin*

## How it works

When you push down on the pedal at the base of the bin, this movement is transferred through a series of linkages and pivots to the lid, causing it to open. This is shown in Figure 2.42.

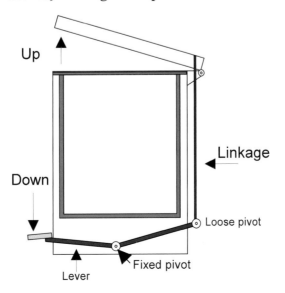

**Figure 2.42** *Drawing of a pedal bin linkage*

**Figure 2.43** *Music stand*

**Figure 2.44** *Folding umbrella*

### Music stand

A music stand incorporates a series of linkages designed to allow the stand to fold away. This is shown in Figure 2.43.

### Folding umbrella

An umbrella is designed to open, lock in position and fold away by means of a series of linkages. These linkages are then used to support the covering material of the umbrella. This is shown in Figure 2.44.

## Designing with linkages

When designing a linkage it is sometimes necessary to think of the mechanism as a 'black box'. With 'black box' design it is important to think of the input and output you want and leave the internal mechanism until later.

**Figure 2.45** *Black box*

The 'black box' in this example could be for a linkage that changes a small input movement into a large output movement. Other examples could be to change a linear input to move in the opposite direction or turn through 90° or change linear motion into rotary motion.

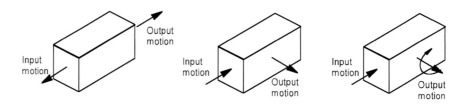

**Figure 2.46** *Black box design*

### Increasing the output movement of a push–pull fixed pivot linkage

If the fixed pivot is at the centre of the vertical link, then the input and output forces will be the same. Where the fixed pivot is off centre, as shown in Figure 2.47 then there will be an increase or decrease in the output force.

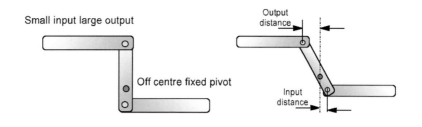

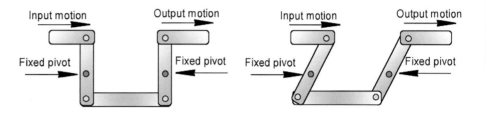

**Figure 2.47** *Fixed pivot points for linkages*

### Rotary linkages

Rotary linkages turn on a fixed axle. The downward input motion is changed into an upward output motion. This is shown in Figure 2.48.

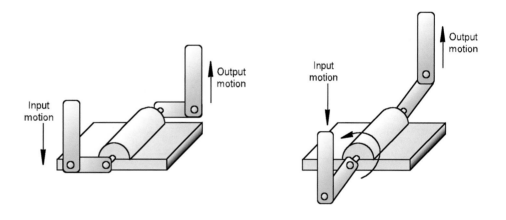

**Figure 2.48** *Rotary linkage*

### Parallel motion linkages

If you make a frame and join the corners with loose pivots, then you will have a parallel linkage.

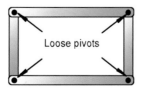

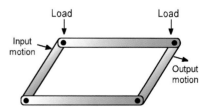

**Figure 2.49** *Parallel motion linkages*

When a load is applied to the top of the linkage it moves downwards. As this happens the opposite sides remain parallel. This type of linkage is used in products like a maintenance platform for a go-kart. This is shown in Figure 2.50.

**Figure 2.50** *Operating the maintenance platform for a go-kart*

# Combining levers and linkages

The accelerator pedal in a car has a series of linkages that connect it to the carburettor. By pushing in the accelerator pedal you are able to open the baffle in the carburettor to allow more petrol into the engine. Some of these components are linkages and others levers. The levers are those components that pivot when a forces is applied. Linkages are those that join one lever to another, transferring motion. This is shown in Figure 2.51.

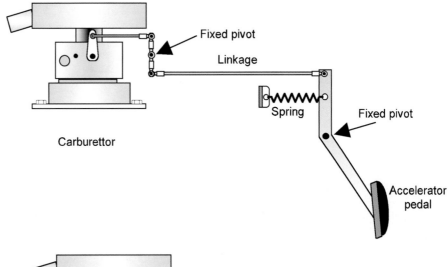

**Figure 2.51** *Position of the accelerator pedal when the car is idling*

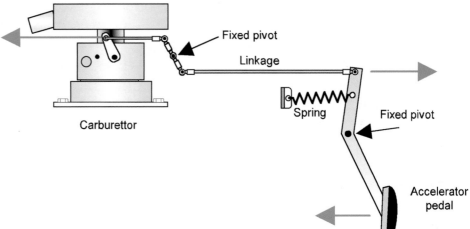

**Figure 2.52** *Position of the accelerator pedal when the car is moving*

When the accelerator pedal is pressed in, the linkage moves the fixed lever on the carburettor to make the car go faster. This is shown in Figure 2.52.

## Graphic symbols for levers and linkages

When you are designing projects which have levers and linkages in them, it is not necessary to draw the actual component. You can save time at the design stage if you use graphic symbols that represent linkages and levers. The graphical symbols used with mechanisms are shown in Figure 2.53.

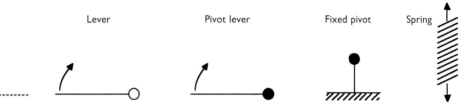

Linkage      Lever      Pivot lever      Fixed pivot      Spring

**Figure 2.53** *Graphic symbols for levers and linkages*

## Diagram for the linkages used in a carburettor

The graphic symbols used in the linkage arrangement for the car accelerator mechanism are shown below in Figure 2.54.

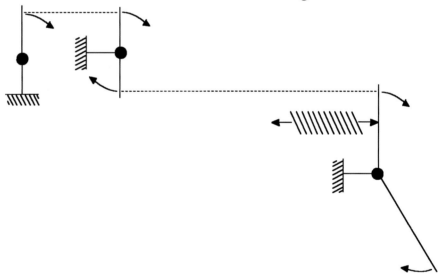

**Figure 2.54** *Drawing the accelerator mechanism for a carburettor using graphical symbols*

Not all mechanisms containing linkages are made from metal. The traditional deck chair was made from beech. The chair contained a three-bar linkage system that could be adjusted to raise and lower the angle of the sitting position. The system is shown in Figure 2.56.

**Figure 2.55** *A wooden deck chair*

**Figure 2.56** *Wooden deck chair using a 3-bar linkage*

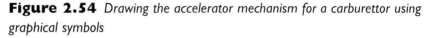

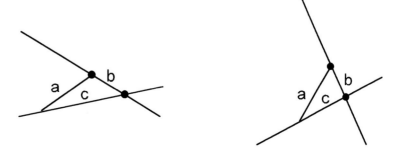

# Jockey pulleys

Jockey pulleys are used to apply tension to the belt where it is not practical to move the drive source to increase tension. Timing belts in car engines often use a jockey pulley to give the desired tension. In this case it would not be possible to slide one-half of the engine away from the other to tension the belt. There are two main types of jockey pulleys, fixed and sprung.

### Fixed jockey pulley

A fixed pulley will require tightening from time to time. This is achieved by means of a slot on the jockey pulley bracket. By loosening the nut you can slide the jockey pulley to increase or decrease the tension on the belt. The nut would then be tightened to maintain the tension.

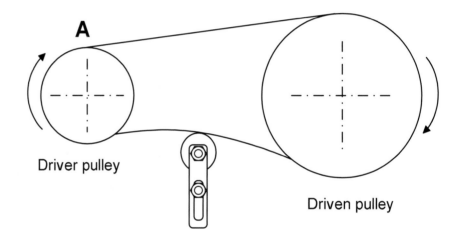

**Figure 2.57** *Fixed jockey pulley*

### Sprung self-adjusting jockey pulley

The sprung self-adjusting jockey pulley has a strong spring that keeps the wheel firmly against the belt. This type of jockey pulley is used when stretching of the belt is a problem or when belt slip is desirable.

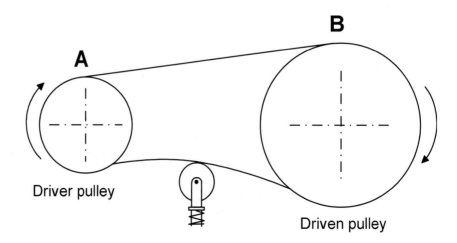

**Figure 2.58** *Sprung or self-adjusting jockey pulley*

### Velocity ratio

$$\text{velocity ratio (VR)} = \frac{\text{distance moved by the effort}}{\text{distance moved by the load}}$$

In the case of belts and pulleys, this would be the same as:

$$\text{velocity ratio (VR)} = \frac{\text{diameter of driven pulley}}{\text{diameter of driver pulley}}$$

If the driver pulley is larger than the driven pulley then the speed of the driven pulley will be greater than that of the driver. This is shown in Figure 2.59.

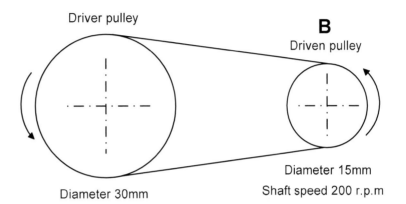

Driver pulley

**B**

Driven pulley

Diameter 15mm
Shaft speed 200 r.p.m

Diameter 30mm

**Figure 2.59** *Driven pulley larger than the driver pulley*

| Example | The pulley system above has a driver pulley of 30 mm diameter and a driven pulley of 15 mm diameter: |
|---|---|

$$VR = \frac{\text{Diameter of driven pulley}}{\text{diameter of driver pulley}} = \frac{15}{30} = \frac{1}{2}$$
$$VR = 1:2$$

### Calculating revs/min

You can use the velocity ratio of driven over driver to calculate the speed (revolutions per minute) of the driver pulley. If you take the same example as before with 200 revs/min, then:

$$\frac{\text{Rotary velocity of driver pulley} \times \text{diameter of driver pulley}}{\text{diameter of driven pulley}}$$

Rotary velocity of driven pulley

$$= \frac{200 \text{ revs/min} \times 30\text{mm}}{15\,\text{mm}} = \frac{200 \times 30}{15} = \frac{6000}{15} = \frac{400}{1}$$

Therefore the velocity of the driven pulley = 400 revs/min

# Worm and wheel

The worm has one tooth that twists round a shaft like a screw. The worm meshes with the wormwheel that is similar to a standard gearwheel. When the worm turns through one revolution the wormwheel moves one tooth. The worm is often found on electric motors turning at high speeds as a means of obtaining a high gear ratio.

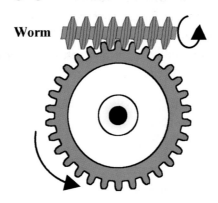

**Figure 2.60** *Worm and wormwheel*

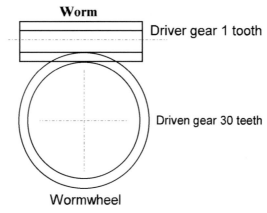

**Figure 2.61** *Symbol for worm and wormwheel*

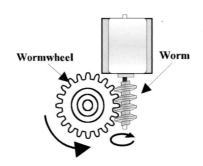

**Figure 2.62**
*Wormwheel and worm gear fixed to a motor*

A wormwheel and worm gear fixed to a small d.c. motor is shown in Figure 2.62. This system can be used to reduce the speed of the motor. In this example, one turn of the motor equals one tooth moved on the wormwheel.

To calculate the gear ratio of a meshed worm and wormwheel

$$\text{gear ratio} = \frac{\text{number of teeth in the driven}}{\text{number of teeth in the driver}}$$

$$\text{gear ratio} = \frac{\text{number of teeth in the wormwheel}}{\text{number of teeth in the worm}}$$

$$\text{gear ratio} = \frac{30}{1}$$

$$\text{gear ratio} = 30{:}1$$

**Figure 2.63** *Picture of a d.c. motor and worm gear*

# Rack and pinion gear system

The rack and pinion is designed to change rotary motion into linear motion or linear motion into rotary motion. The pinion gear shown in Figure 2.64 has 30 teeth. As it turns through one revolution it will cause the rack to travel along in a linear path for a distance of 30 teeth.

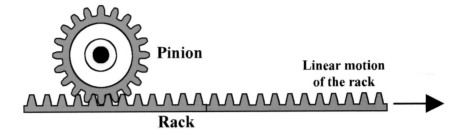

**Figure 2.64** *Rack and Pinion*

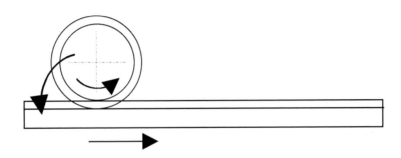

**Figure 2.65** *Graphic symbol for a rack and pinion*

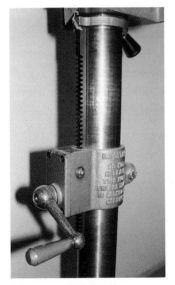

**Figure 2.66** *Close-up view of the rack and pinion*

**Figure 2.67** *Drilling machine with a rack and pinion gear*

## Rack and Pinion used in technology products

Rack and pinion gears can be found on a drilling machine. The table is raised and lowered by means of the rack and pinion. The pinion gear is housed in the handle unit and the rack is fixed to the column of the drilling machine. This system is shown in Figure 2.66.

## Stand for a portable electric drill

### Design situation

When using a portable electric drill it is difficult to hold it steady. This often results in the drill bit drifting over to one side during the drilling operation. There is a need for a stand that would securely hold a portable electric drill when drilling holes.

### Solution

The solution was a portable electric drill stand with a rack and pinion. When the handle was pulled down, the pinion gear ran in the rack. This enabled the drill to move down.

The portable drilling machine was held in position by a compression spring. The spring was manufactured in the school workshop from malleable spring alloy wire. The wire was wound round a wooden former, removed and placed in a kiln to heat-treat the alloy. This process transformed the malleable alloy wire into a spring. The final arrangement is shown in Figure 2.68.

**Figure 2.68** *A stand for a portable electric drill*

## Ratchet and pawl

The ratchet and pawl is designed to allow movement in one direction. The ratchet is a wheel with saw-shaped teeth on its edge. The pawl is designed to engage in the teeth. The pawl is held firmly against the ratchet with a spring.

The ratchet and pawl can be found on tennis nets where it is used to raise the net to the correct height. It can also be found on some 4 × 4 off road vehicles where it is part of the winch mechanism found above the front bumper or on boat trailers, where it is used to pull the boat onto the trailer. Examples of these are shown in figures 2.69 and 2.70.

**96**

**Figure 2.69** *A ratchet and pawl used on a boat trailer*

**Figure 2.70** *A winch*

The pawl is designed to allow for rotation in one direction only. The pawl engages in the teeth of the ratchet during rotation by moving down into the tooth. A spring is often used to pull the pawl into position. The arrow on the ratchet indicates the direction of rotation.

### Tennis-court net adjustment

The drawing is of a tennis court net where the ratchet and pawl is used to raise the net to the regulation height. When the handle is turned, the ratchet tightens the top of the net while the pawl prevents the net from slipping. This is shown in Figure 2.72.

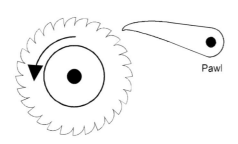 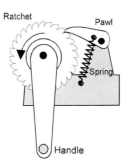

**Figure 2.71** *Ratchet and pawl*

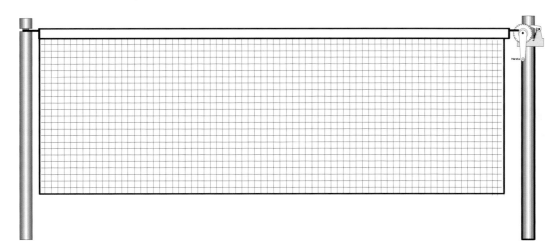

**Figure 2.72** *Tennis-court net*

# Velocity ratio of gears

The drawing in Fig. 2.73 shows two meshed gears. The large gear wheel B has 40 teeth and the smaller pinion gear A has 20 teeth. If the driver gear B completes one revolution the driven gear will turn two revolutions. In this simple gear train, the driver provides the effort while the driven asserts the load.

$$\text{velocity ratio (VR)} = \frac{\text{distance moved by the load}}{\text{distance moved by the effort}}$$

$$\text{velocity ratio (VR)} = \frac{1 \text{ revolution}}{2 \text{ revolutions}}$$

$$\text{velocity ratio (VR)} = \frac{1}{2} = 1{:}2$$

**97**

**Figure 2.74** *Meshed gears used on a test rig*

The velocity ratio for this simple gear train is 1:2. One revolution of the driver equals two revolutions of the driven. Velocity ratio and gear ratio are basically the same thing.

If you calculate the gear ratio and compare it to the velocity ratio you will find both are the same ratio.

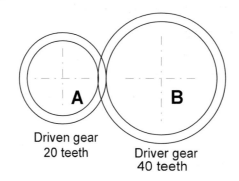

Driven gear
20 teeth

Driver gear
40 teeth

**Figure 2.73** *Meshed gears*

| Example | **Gear ratio for the gear train in Figure 2.73** |
|---|---|

$$\text{gear ratio (GR)} = \frac{\text{number of teeth in the driven}}{\text{number of teeth in the driver}}$$

$$\text{gear ratio (GR)} = \frac{20}{40} = \frac{1}{2} \text{ or } 1{:}2$$

## Velocity of the driven gear

To calculate velocity of the driven gear you will need to know the revolutions per minute of the **driver** gear and the **velocity ratio**. In Figure 2.75, the driver gear is turning at 100 revolutions per minute. The driver gear has 40 teeth and the driven gear has 20 teeth. When you know this it is possible to calculate the velocity of the driven gear.

velocity of driven gear =

$$\frac{\text{number of teeth on driver gear} \times \text{velocity of driver gear}}{\text{number of teeth on driven gear}}$$

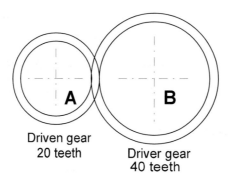

Driven gear
20 teeth

Driver gear
40 teeth

**Figure 2.75** *Driver gear turning at 100 revs/min*

**Figure 2.76** *A pinion and gear wheel*

$$\text{velocity of driven gear} = \frac{40 \times 100}{20}$$

$$\text{velocity of driven gear} = \frac{4000}{20} = 200 \text{ revs/min}$$

## Calculating gear ratio/velocity ratio of a gear train

### *Calculating Gear Ratio*

The gear train shown in Figure 2.77 incorporates a small d.c. motor with a worm gear rotating at 2800 revolutions per minute (revs/min). The driver gear has 20 teeth and the driven gear has 40 teeth.

The calculations involve finding the **gear ratio** for the gear train and the **velocity** of the driven gear C.

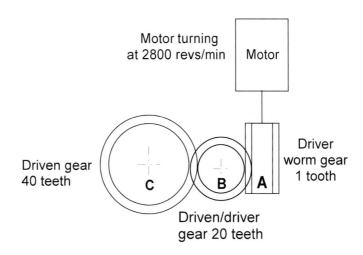

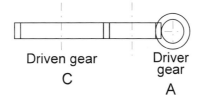

**Figure 2.77** *Calculating gear ratio*

$$\text{gear ratio} = \frac{\text{number of teeth in the driven gear}}{\text{number of teeth in the driver gear}}$$

$$\text{gear ratio} = \frac{\text{number of teeth in the driven gear B}}{\text{number of teeth in the driver gear A}}$$

$$\times$$

$$\frac{\text{number of teeth in the driven gear C}}{\text{number of teeth in the driver gear B}}$$

$$\text{gear ratio} = \frac{B}{A} \times \frac{C}{B}$$

$$\text{gear ratio} = \frac{20}{1} \times \frac{40}{20} = \frac{800}{20} = \frac{80}{2} = \frac{40}{1}$$

**gear ratio = 40:1**

This means that for every 40 turns of the worm gear A, gear C will turn once.

### Velocity of the driven gear

Velocity of driven gear =

$$\frac{\text{number of teeth on driver gear} \times \text{velocity of driver gear (revs/min)}}{\text{number of teeth on driven gear}}$$

$$\text{Velocity of driven gear} = \frac{A}{B} \times \frac{B}{C} \times \frac{2800}{1} = \frac{1}{20} \times \frac{20}{40} \times \frac{2800}{1}$$

$$= \frac{70}{1} = 70 \text{ revs/min}$$

Velocity of driven gear = 70 revs/min

# Mechanical advantage of gears

Mechanical advantage happens when the force of one gear produces a greater force on the other gear.

In gear trains, the tooth of one gear in contact with the tooth of another gear applies a force.

The principle of the lever is at work here. The tooth can be thought of as a lever that has one end at the centre of the shaft and the other at the end of the tooth. When the small lever pushes down on the end of the large lever, an increase in force will be present at the centre shaft of the large gear. As this force is rotating about a centre point, we call it torque. When there is an increase or decrease in torque the gears are said to be torque converters. When no increase of decrease in torque is present, these gears are said to be torque transmitters. When there is an increase in torque as shown in Figure 2.78 then there will also be a decrease in the rotational velocity of the driven gear. A decrease in torque will result in an increase in rotational velocity.

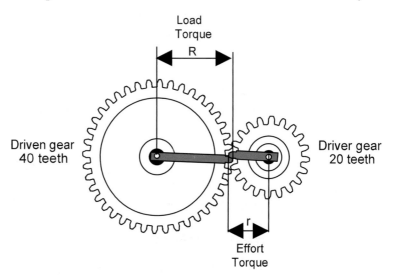

**Figure 2.78** *Torque present in two meshed gears*

### Calculating mechanical advantage of two gears

To calculate the mechanical advantage of the two meshed gears shown in Figure 2.78 you would use the formula:

$$MA = \frac{\text{load torque}}{\text{effort torque}}$$

Torque can be found by multiplying the force by the radius of the gear wheel.

torque = force $\times$ radius of the gear wheel

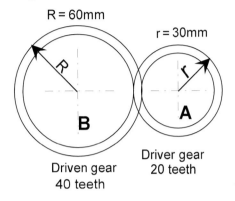

**Figure 2.79** *Torque*

$$MA = \frac{\text{load torque}}{\text{effort torque}} = \frac{F \times R}{F \times r} = \frac{R}{r}$$

MA for the example in Figure 2.79

$$MA = \frac{\text{radius of driven gear}}{\text{radius of driver gear}}$$

$$MA = \frac{60}{30} = \frac{2}{1} = 2:1$$

### Projects incorporating gears

The following project was the work of a year-11 student and shows an application for a simple gear train and worm gear.

#### Design situation

A student won a crystal trophy that she wanted to display. The display unit had to rotate to show the full effect of the crystal in the light.

#### Solution

The final solution used a simple gear train incorporating three gears.

The drive source was a small DC motor. The problem was how to slow the final gear down to the required revolutions. A worm gear was chosen and was fixed to the shaft of a small electric d.c. motor.

#### How it works

When the power is switched on, the d.c. motor rotates. The worm gear meshes with the first gear in the gear train, which is a wormwheel. This transmits rotation to the idler gear. The idler gear meshes with the final driven gear. The disc-shaped platform was an old CD fixed to the gear with two-sided tape. The small MDF (Medium Density Fibre-board) disc provided clearance between the top of the shafts and the CD.

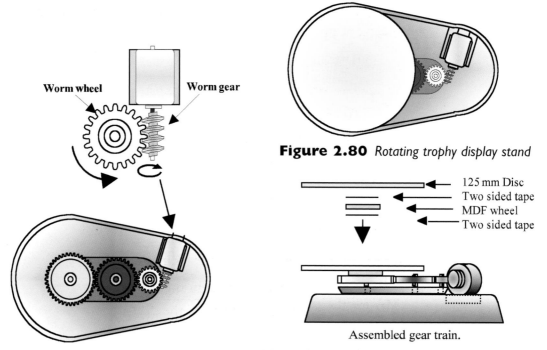

**Figure 2.80** *Rotating trophy display stand*

125 mm Disc
Two sided tape
MDF wheel
Two sided tape

Assembled gear train.

**Figure 2.81** *Adding the worm gear and drive motor*

**Figure 2.82** *Assembled gear train*

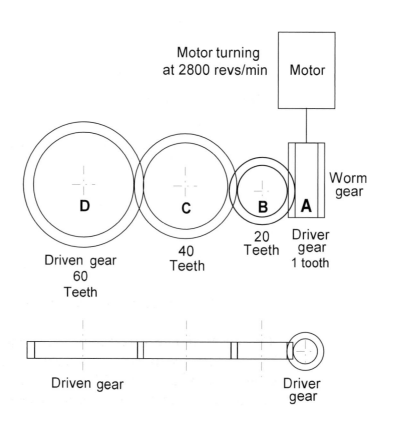

Motor turning at 2800 revs/min | Motor

Worm gear

D | C | B | A

Driven gear 60 Teeth

40 Teeth

20 Teeth

Driver gear 1 tooth

Driven gear

Driver gear

**Figure 2.83** *Simple gear train used with the rotating display*

### Calculating the gear/velocity ratio for the rotating display

*Calculating gear ratio*

The method for calculating the gear ratio and velocity of the rotating display shown in Figure 2.83 are set out below.

### The d.c. motor

A small d.c. motor turning at 2800 revs/min was chosen as the means of driving the display.

### Simple geartrain

After calculating different gear permutations, it was decided to use the following gear train:

- A worm gear 1 tooth.
- B driven/driver gear 20 teeth.
- C driven/driver gear 40 teeth.
- D driven gear 60 teeth.

The final calculations are set out below.

### Gear ratio for the simple gear train

$$\text{gear ratio} = \frac{\text{number of teeth in the driven gear}}{\text{number of teeth in the driver gear}}$$

$$\text{gear ratio} = \frac{B}{A} \times \frac{C}{B} \times \frac{D}{C}$$

$$\text{gear ratio} = \frac{20}{1} \times \frac{40}{20} \times \frac{60}{40} = \frac{48\,000}{800} = \frac{480}{8} = \frac{60}{1}$$

**gear ratio = 60:1**

### Velocity of the driven gear

velocity of driven gear =

$$\frac{\text{number of teeth on driver gear} \times \text{velocity of driver gear}}{\text{number of teeth on driven gear}}$$

$$\text{velocity of driven gear} = \frac{A}{B} \times \frac{B}{C} \times \frac{C}{D} \times \frac{2800}{1}$$

$$= \frac{1}{20} \times \frac{20}{40} \times \frac{40}{60} \times \frac{2800}{1} = \frac{46.66}{1} = 46.66$$

velocity of driven gear = 46.66 revs/min

### The circuit for the rotating display

The display was operated by a toggle switch. When the switch was turned on, the motor would turn. A 1.5 V battery was chosen to turn the motor at its lowest output speed.

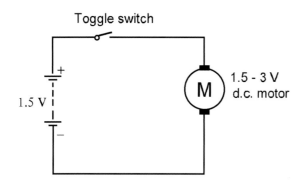

**Figure 2.84** *Circuit diagram*

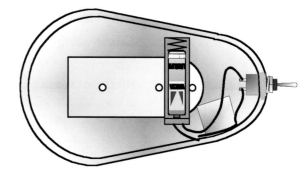

**Figure 2.85** *Drawing of the underside of the project*

### Housing the circuit

The circuit was housed in a vacuum-formed base below the gear train. A piece of 6 mm MDF was vacuum formed into the base. This enabled the shafts for the gear train and the battery holder to be fixed securely in position. An under view of the shell housing is shown in Figure 2.85.

### Completed project

The completed project rotated at 46.66 revs/min, which was fine for what she wanted the display to do.

## Bevel Gears

Bevel gears are used in mechanisms where two shafts are at 90° to each other and when a direct drive is required between the input shaft and the output shaft.

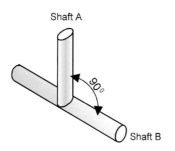

**Figure 2.86** *Input and output shafts at 90 degrees*

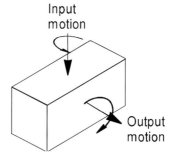

**Figure 2.87** *Black box*

Bevel gears are cone shaped with the teeth cut on the edges of the cone. They are used in pairs to create a direct drive between input and output shafts mounted at 90° to each other.

An example of a pair of bevel gears used on a hand-operated drilling machine is shown in Figure 2.88.

**Figure 2.88** *A pair of meshed bevel gears*

### Graphic symbol

The graphic symbol for a bevel gear A is shown in Figure 2.89.

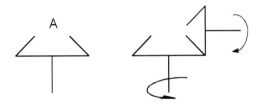

**Figure 2.89** *Graphic Symbol for bevel gears*

Meshed bevel gears incorporate two symbols that come into contact to show the position of the mesh. It is normal to see arrows on the symbol indicating the direction of rotation

## Compound gears

Gears are designed to turn shafts. A simple gear would be one single gear fixed to one shaft.

**Figure 2.90** *Simple gear on one shaft*

**Figure 2.91** *Meshed simple gears train*

Compound gears have two or more gears fixed to the same shaft. With this type of gear each gear wheel in the compound will have a different number of teeth.

In Figure 2.92, when the shaft with the compound gears on it

**105**

completes one revolution, the small gearwheel has passed point A once. When this happens all 20 teeth will have completed one revolution.

The large gear fixed to the same shaft will have also completed one revolution but this time 40 teeth will have passed point A.

Point A

**Figure 2.92** *Compound gear*    **Figure 2.93** *Meshed compound gear train*

### Graphic symbol for compound gears

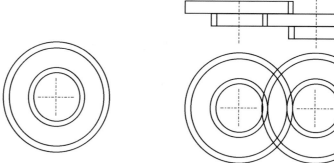

**Figure 2.94** *Compound gear*    **Figure 2.95** *Compound gear train*

### Compound geartrain

In a compound geartrain, the shafts will be rotating at different speeds. If you consider the three-shaft compound gear train shown in Figure 2.98, then as the driver shaft completes one-revolution, 40 teeth on the outer gear will have passed point A. As the driver gear is in contact with the middle 20 teeth compound gear at point B, this gear will also turn through 40 teeth. This will mean that point B will have rotated twice. The outer teeth on the middle gear will also go round twice, which means 80 teeth will pass point D. 80 teeth passing point D will also mean 80 teeth passed point C. The 20 teeth gear on the driven gear will rotate four times to allow 80 teeth to pass point C. Simply, this means that one revolution of the driver gear results in two revolutions of the middle gear, which results in four revolutions of the driven gear. Resulting in shaft of the driven gear C rotating four times as fast as the driver shaft A.

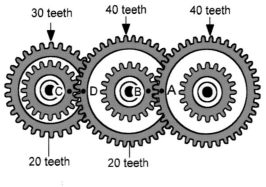

**Figure 2.96** *Compound gear train*

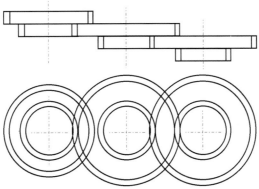

**Figure 2.97** *Graphic symbol for a compound gear train*

**Graphic symbol for a three shaft compound gear train**

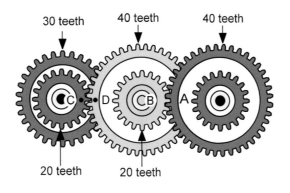

**Figure 2.98** *A compound gear train used on a centre lathe*

| Example | Building a compound gear train with a gear ratio 5:1 |

The gear wheel and compound gear shown in figure 2.99 has the driver gear (A) fixed to the motor and one compound gear (B,C) fixed to the output. This combination will reduce the speed of output shaft by a ratio of 5:1.

**Calculating Gear Ratio**

$$\text{Gear Ratio} = \frac{\text{Number of teeth in the driven gear}}{\text{Number of teeth in the driver gear}}$$

$$\text{Gear Ratio} = \frac{B}{A}$$

$$\text{Gear Ratio} = \frac{50}{10} = \frac{5}{1}$$

$$\text{Gear Ratio} = 5:1$$

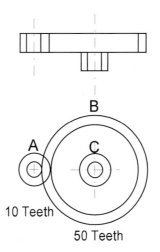

**Figure 2.99** *Symbol for the gear train*

### Calculating the Velocity for the gearbox

If the motor is turning at 2800 revs/min. Then:

Velocity of driven gear =

$$\frac{\text{Number of teeth on driver gear x velocity of driver gear}}{\text{Number of teeth on driven gear}}$$

$$\text{Velocity of driven gear} = \frac{A}{B} \times \frac{2800}{1} = \frac{10 \times 2800}{50} \quad \frac{1}{1} = \frac{560}{1} = 560$$

Velocity of driven gear = 560 revs/min

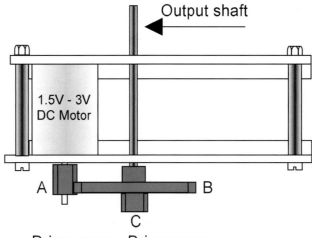

**Figure 2.100** *View of the assembled gearbox*

Using the same modular gears and matrix plates as used in example 1, it is possible to design and build a gearbox with gear ratio of 625:1.

This example uses a gear wheel on the motor and four compound gears to reduce the speed of the output shaft by a ratio of 625:1. The motor is still turning at 2800 revs/min.

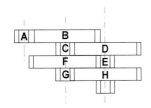

### Calculating Gear Ratio

$$\text{Gear Ratio} = \frac{\text{Number of teeth in the driven gear}}{\text{Number of teeth in the driver gear}}$$

$$\text{Gear Ratio} = \frac{B}{A} \times \frac{D}{C} \times \frac{F}{E} \times \frac{H}{G}$$

$$\text{Gear Ratio} = \frac{50}{10} \times \frac{50}{10} \times \frac{50}{10} \times \frac{50}{10} = \frac{6250000}{10000} = \frac{625}{1}$$

$$\text{Gear Ratio} = 625:1$$

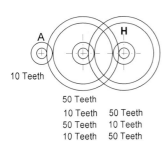

10 Teeth

50 Teeth
10 Teeth    50 Teeth
50 Teeth    10 Teeth
10 Teeth    50 Teeth

**Figure 2.101** *Symbol for the compound gear train*

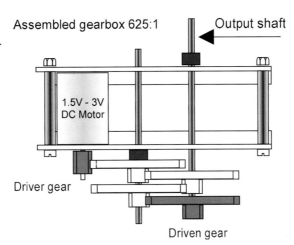

Assembled gearbox 625:1    Output shaft

1.5V - 3V DC Motor

Driver gear

Driven gear

**Figure 2.102** *Drawing of the assembled gearbox*

### Calculating the velocity of the driven gear with a gear ratio of 625:1

$$\text{Velocity of driven gear} = \frac{\text{Number of teeth on driver gear} \times \text{velocity of driver gear}}{\text{Number of teeth on driven gear}}$$

$$\text{Velocity of driven gear} = \frac{A \times C \times E \times G \times 2800}{B \quad D \quad F \quad H \quad 1}$$

$$\text{Velocity of driven gear} = \frac{10 \times 10 \times 10 \times 10 \times 2800}{50 \quad 50 \quad 50 \quad 50 \quad 1} =$$

$$\frac{1 \times 2800}{625 \quad 1} = 4.48$$

Velocity of driven gear = 4.48 revs/min

The following project was a students GCSE coursework project.

### Situation

A local sports shop had contacted the school's Technology and Design department with a design problem. They wanted a large slowly rotating display on which they could display trophies. The display was to be located in the shop window.

### Customer specification

A few of the main specification points from the shop owner were:

1. The display must rotate approximately once every minute
2. Fit into a space 400mm square
3. Should not obstruct the view of the rotating trophies
4. Run continuously from either a battery pack or sealed plug-in transformer
5. Hold between 1- 4 trophies
6. Be a high quality product
7. Cost of material to be not more than £50

### Solution

The final solution had clear acrylic shelf fixed to vertical acrylic pillar. The complete acrylic upper structure was located on a vertical steel shaft. This is shown in figure 2.103.

**Figure 2.103** *Rotating trophy display stand*

## Mechanism detail for the rotating trophy display stand

### Motor

The gearbox was driven by a small 3 volt d.c. motor that rotated at 3125 revs/min.

### Gearbox

The gearbox was built from a matrix gear kit which was assembled to give a reduction ratio of 625:1.

**Figure 2.104** *Assembled gearbox*

### Drive Shafts

The output shaft was 4mm steel with the final drive shaft extending 25mm beyond the pulley.

### Final drive

The final drive was a round belt. The reason for this was its ability to slip if the rotating display became obstructed. The driver pulley was 10mm in diameter with the final output driven pulley being larger at 50mm diameter. This gave a pulley ratio of 5:1. These pulleys and a gear ratio of 625:1 gave an output shaft speed of approximately 1 rev/min.

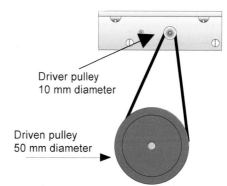

**Figure 2.105** *Top view of the pulleys*

## Resisting downward and side forces

### Thrust bearing

A thrust bearing was used to reduce the friction when the display was filled with trophies.

### Needle bearings

Needle bearings were used to reduce the friction on the shaft from lateral forces.

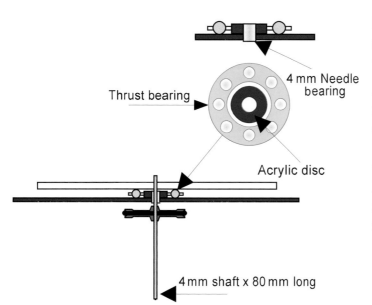

**Figure 2.106** *Thrust and needle bearing assembly*

## Section details of the completed assembly

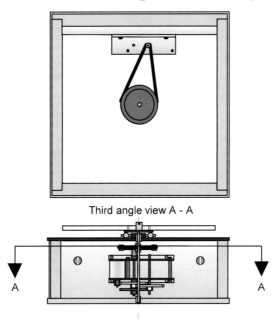

Third angle view A - A

**Figure 2.107** *Sectional view of the gearbox fixed to the base unit*

### Base unit

The base unit was made from mahogany. This was given several coats of varnish to bring out the natural texture and colouring in the grain. The top was made from 5mm blue acrylic to match the shop colours. The top was increased in thickness at the centre to secure and align the needle bearing. This is shown in figure 2.107. The needle bearings were an interference fit on both the top and bottom of the box to reduce lateral friction.

### Brass bush

A plastic wheel with a brass bush was use to ensure a vertical fixing between the shaft, bottom clear acrylic disc and base unit. This is shown in figure 2.108.

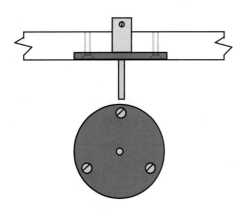

**Figure 2.108** *Fixing the brass bush*

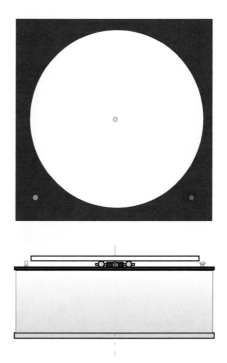

**Figure 2.109** *View of the assembled base unit*

# CHAPTER THREE    Higher Microprocessor/Computer Control

The use of microprocessors and computers in control situations has become increasingly popular over the last number of years. This has been largely due to the availability and ease of use of new software packages coming onto the market. The use of computers at Key Stage 3 has created an awareness of the versatility of computers in control situations.

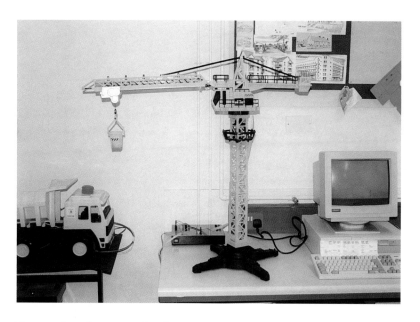

**Figure 3.1** *Computer controlled crane*

Recently, the use of microprocessors as stand-along devices has made them very popular with students at Key Stage 4 and Advanced Level. The reason for this has been mainly due to the introduction of the PIC (Peripheral Interface Controller). These ICs have become cheaper and the software to program them has become readily available.

PICs have become very popular with students for coursework projects as, once the circuit is understood, its application is largely limited to your ability to program it. This will enable you to design projects that in the past would have required a complex circuit design.

Downloading your program to the PIC is a simple matter using one of the many serial PIC programmer boards available from educational technology suppliers. The boards shown in Figure 3.2 are programmed via the serial port on your computer using commercial software.

The first part of this chapter will explain digital and analogue signals for computer control, while the second part will focus on PICs.

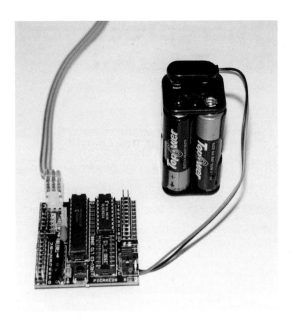 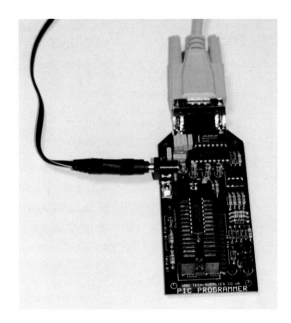

**Figure 3.2** *PIC programmer boards*

# Flowcharts for digital input/outputs and analogue input signals

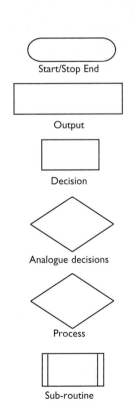

**Figure 3.3** *Flowchart symbols*

A flowchart is used to help you to plan the sequence of your microprocessor/computer control program.

There are a number of common symbols used in a flowchart to represent conditions such as start, stop, output, decisions, wait, analogue inputs and loops. The symbols are shown in Figure 3.3.

### Example of a flowchart

The flowchart shown in Figure 3.4 will use the start, stop, decision, process and output symbols.

The function of each symbol is listed below.
- The Start symbol is used at the beginning of your program/sub-routine or procedure.
- The Stop symbol is used to stop your program.
- The End symbol is used to end a sub-routine or procedure.
- The Output symbol is to turn on or off outputs.
- The decision symbol is used for all inputs. Digital inputs signals, comparing the value of variables in a loop, are all inputs. Decision symbols usually have a yes/no part to them which denote whether or not the decision has happened.
- The decision cell is used to enter a numerical value of an analogue signal (referred to as ADVAL or A0 depending on the software). The computer software will compare this numerical value and respond accordingly. Decision symbols usually have a yes/no part to them and denote whether or not an analogue numerical value has been reached. These cells are called **compare cells** in some software packages.

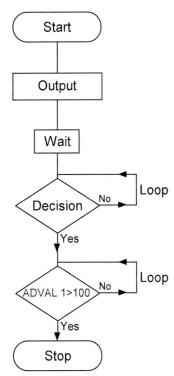

**Figure 3.4** *Flowchart*

- The Process symbol is used for time delays and variables.
- The Sub-routine symbol is used for calling a Sub-routine into your main program. Some software packages call this Macros or Procedures.

### Output summary

In addition to using the correct symbol in your flowchart it is necessary to give a summary of what you want to happen in each cell of your flowchart.

If you wished to write a program to turn on bit 0 you would have to give the output cell a name and specify the condition of each bit. This is shown in Figure 3.5. The summary is then shortened to O/P 0 0 0 0 0 0 0 1.

**Figure 3.5** *Output summary*

### Decision summary

Decisions are mainly associated with inputs. If you wished to include a decision in your program that waited until input bit 0 was high then you would give the decision cell a name and specify the condition of the input bit. The program would check to see if this condition was true and if it was, the program would do something, if not it would keep checking until it was true. An example is shown in Figure 3.6. Once again the summary would be shortened to read I/P · · · · · · · 1.

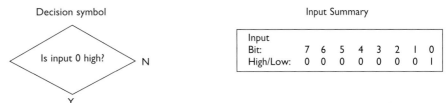

**Figure 3.6** *Input summary*

### Analogue summary

You will have four analogue channels available to you. It is possible to use one or all of these in your program. For example, if you had an LDR and a thermistor in your circuit it would be possible to use two of the analogue channels e.g. A1 and A2 (ADVAL 1 and 2) in your program. Depending on the software you are using, each channel has a maximum numerical value. Most software designers use the value of 1000.

**Figure 3.7** *Analogue summary*

Symbol     Wait summary

| Wait 3 | Wait 3 seconds |

**Figure 3.6** *Wait summary*

### *Wait summary*

If you wished to have a time delay in your program flowchart, you would use the wait symbol. It is usual to specify the wait in seconds or parts of a second. An example of the summary for this is shown in Figure 3.6.

## Sub-routines

A sub-routine is a program written outside the main program and called into the main program as and when it is needed. These are referred to in some software packages as macros. The important point to remember with a sub-routine is to use precisely the same name in both the main program and in the sub-routine.

Sub-routines are very useful and can save you time when programming. They are often used when you need to repeat a series of lines more than once. Rather than writing the lines time and time again, they can be written once, defined as a sub-routine and then called into your main program.

| Example | Designing a child's toy |

### *Design situation*

The student was asked to design and make a toy for a young child. The toy had to have movement and flashing lights.

### *Solution*

The solution was a rotating carousel that had six LEDs. The LEDs came on in series each one staying on until a full cycle was completed. The LEDs had to repeat this pattern for twenty revolutions of the carousel. The input was in two parts, a push-to-make switch to start the carousel and a reed switch on the base to count the revolutions. The magnet was fixed to the rotating base of the ride. A picture of the final project is shown in Figure 3.8.

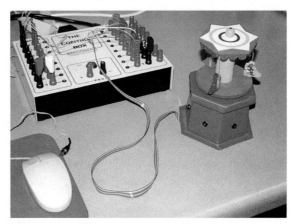

**Figure 3.8** *Computer controlled carousel*

### *Flowchart for the carousel*

The main program is started when an input is detected at input 0. As the program runs, it waits for 5 seconds then switches on the motor turning the carousel. Next, the carousel is allowed to turn until the LEDs have come on twenty times. During each rotation the LEDs come on in series until the last one, at which point they all go out. The LEDs program was written as a macro/procedure and called into the main program using the name 'Lights'. The flowchart for the main program and the macro/sub-routine is shown in figures 3.9 and 3.10. The flowchart summary for both is shown in Figures 3.11 and 3.12.

### Variables (counting routine)

The program was designed to turn on the sub routine 'Lights' twenty times. This was possible by using a counting routine. Just before the program reached the macro Lights a variable A (counting routine) was set to zero. At the end of each macro 'Lights' the program waited 0.5 seconds before moving down to increase the count of 'A' by one (A=A+1). The next line in the program compared the value of the variable 'A'. If it was greater than or equal to 20 (A>=20) then the program moved out of loop 2 and switched off the carousel.

## Main program flowchart

### Sub-routine flowchart

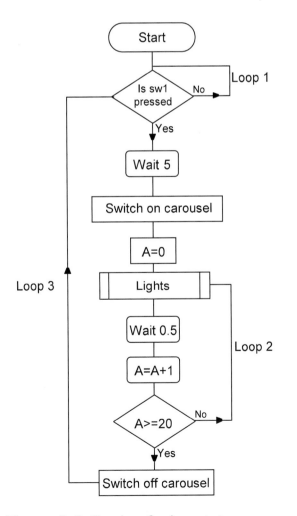

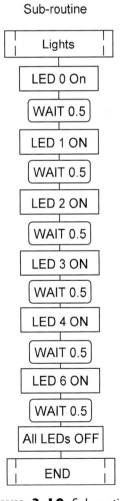

**Figure 3.9** *Flowchart for the main program*

**Figure 3.10** *Sub-routine flowchart*

## Main program and sub-routine summary for the carousel

*Main program summary*

| Cell Name | Program function | Input/Output state |
|---|---|---|
| Start | | |
| Loop 1 | GOTO | |
| Is sw1 pressed | Input Decision | I/P .... 1 |
| Wait 5 second | Time Loop | |
| Switch on carousel | Output | O/P 0 0 0 0 0 0 0 1 |
| A=0 | Let A=0 | |
| Lights | Sub-routine | |
| Wait 0.5 seconds | Time Loop | |
| A=A+1 | Increase value of A by 1 | |
| Loop 2 | GOTO | |
| Is A>=20 | Decision | I/P A>= 20 |
| Switch off carousel | Output | O/P 0 0 0 0 0 0 0 0 |
| Loop 3 | Repeat forever | |

**Figure 3.11** *Flowchart summary for the main program*

*Sub-routine summary*

| Cell Name | Program function | Input/Output state |
|---|---|---|
| Lights | Start sub-routine | |
| LED 1 ON | Output | O/P 0 0 0 0 0 0 1 1 |
| Wait 0.5 seconds | Time loop | |
| LED 2 ON | Output | O/P 0 0 0 0 0 1 1 1 |
| Wait 0.5 seconds | Time loop | |
| LED 3 ON | Output | O/P 0 0 0 0 1 1 1 1 |
| Wait 0.5 seconds | Time loop | |
| LED 4 ON | Output | O/P 0 0 0 1 1 1 1 1 |
| Wait 0.5 seconds | Time loop | |
| LED 5 ON | Output | O/P 0 0 1 1 1 1 1 1 |
| Wait 0.5 seconds | Time loop | |
| LED 6 ON | Output | O/P 0 1 1 1 1 1 1 1 |
| Wait 0.5 seconds | Time loop | |
| All LEDs OFF | Output | O/P 0 0 0 0 0 0 0 0 |
| END | End and return to main program | |

**Figure 3.12** *Flowchart summary for sub-routine*

# Analogue signals

An analogue signal is one where the voltage is constantly rising and falling. This is in contrast to a digital signal where the voltage is either high or low (on/off). An example of an analogue signal would be a home lighting dimmer switch. As the knob is turned the light will glow bright or dim. This is in contrast to a rocker switch that is designed to produce an on/off digital signal. Another example would be the volume control knob on your radio. By turning the knob the volume increases or decreases.

As computers are designed to work on digital signals only, it is not possible to feed an analogue signal directly into the computer. It will be necessary to change the analogue signal to a series of digital signals. This is called analogue to digital conversion or A-D conversion.

## Analogue to digital conversion

Inside your computer there will be an A-D chip designed to convert analogue signals into a series of digital signals. If you have ever used a joystick then you have used an analogue sensor where the signal was converted to a digital one so that the computer could read it.

## How it works

The A-D chip will read a reference voltage. If your computer is fitted with a BBC I/O (input/output) card this will be 1.8 V. The returning signal voltage is compared by the compute. If it is 1.8 V. then the computer will convert this to 65550 digital signals (digits). If the retuning signal was 0.9 V, then the computer will convert this to 32775 digits (half of 65550). This is shown in Figure 3.13. Some software packages use the number 1000 to make it easier for you to program. In this case the returning voltage would be displayed as 500. You can use this number in your program to tell the computer to do something if this number is present.

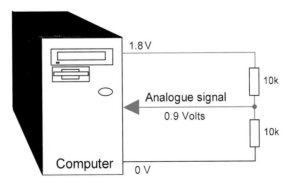

**Figure 3.13** *Analogue interface circuit*

## Building an analogue interface

The circuit shown in Figure 3.14 uses a potential divider with two resistors in series. The voltage drop across each resistor will depend on the value of the resistor. The voltage drop can be calculated using the formula voltage drop $= R_1 \times$ supply voltage$/(R_1 + R_2)$. In the example used in Figure 3.14 the voltage drop at $R_1$ is equal to 3.2 V. By connecting a wire to the middle of the potential divider it is possible to obtain a voltage of 1.8 volts.

This is usually the maximum voltage you can send back into the analogue channel of the computer. It is now possible to connect a series of sensors between point A and the zero volts rail.

Not all analogue interfaces provide you with 1.8 V. Some, like the BBC computer or computers with a BBC I/O fitted card, will output a reference voltage of 5 V at the analogue ports. If this is the case you must use two potential dividers. The first will give you the important 1.8 V and the second will provide the analogue signal. Building a potential divider is explained in detail in the electronics section of this book.

As with all connections to the computer you must check the specification of your computer before making a direct connection to it. If you are unsure, have the work done by a trained expert or, better still, use a commercial analogue interface.

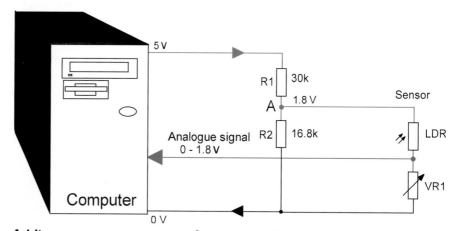

**Figure 3.14** *Building and analogue interface for the BBC I/O card*

**Adding sensors to your analogue circuit**

The 1.8 V obtained from the 5 V coming out of the computer can now be used to make a potential divider that will be the analogue sensor. The analogue sensor $R_3$ could be used to detect heat (thermistor), light (LDR) or a joystick to play games (variable resistor). The lower resistor $R_4$ can be fixed or variable depending on what you plan to use the interface for. Some commercial interfaces are sealed and only allow you to add the sensor $R_3$ to the circuit. This prevents any damage happening to the interface or computer. While others require you to build a potential divider circuit as shown in Figure 3.15.

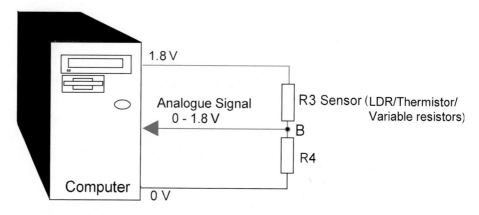

**Figure 3.15** *Adding a sensor to the analogue circuit*

# ADVAL channels

When programming in high-level language such as basic, the command ADVAL is used to recognise an analogue signal coming into your computer. Most computers will have four analogue (ADVAL 1–4) channels, allowing you to connect up to four sensors to the computer at any one time. Each sensor will be connected as shown in Figure 3.15. Most interfaces have 4 mm sockets to allow you to plug in the sensors. This is shown in Figure 3.16.

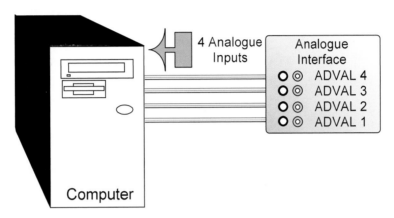

**Figure 3.16** *Analogue interface*

## Design situation

The parents of a technology student have a greenhouse which is used to raise plants from seed. During the early part of the season there is a danger of frost damaging the young plants. There is also the problem of overheating in the greenhouse on sunny days. The student was asked to design and build an environmental control system to overcome these two extremes of hot and cold.

## Solution

**Figure 3.17** *Picture of a greenhouse*

The solution incorporated computer control to monitor and control the environment. A thermistor was placed in the greenhouse and connected through an analogue interface back to the computer. When the temperature was greater than 25° C, a cooling fan came on. The same sensor was used to bring on a heater when the temperature fell below 10° C. Before the final solution was installed it was modelled to evaluate and improve the design. The model is shown in Figure 3.18. The model incorporated a small cooling fan fixed to a d.c. motor and a heat lamp acted as a heater.

## Selecting the analogue sensor

**Figure 3.18** *Modelling the environment*

An NTC 20 k disc thermistor was selected for sensing the temperature. This was connected to analogue channel 1 (ADVAL 1) on the interface. This is shown in Figure 3.19.

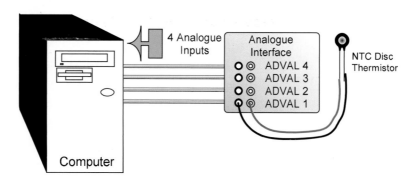

**Figure 3.19** *Connecting the thermistor to the analogue interface*

### Calibrating the thermistor signal

The thermistor was connected to the analogue interface. The software package was set up to detect the signal. The software used a digital scale of 0–1000. A thermometer and the thermistor were placed in a box. The temperature inside the box was lowered to 10° C and a reading of 290 was recorded. The temperature was allowed to rise to 25° C and a reading of 380 was recorded. These two numbers were noted and would be used later in the program.

| Temperature | Reading |
| --- | --- |
| 10° C | 290 |
| 25° C | 380 |

*Calibrate Readings*

### Connecting the digital inputs and outputs to the interface

For the model a 12 V d.c. motor acted as the cooling fan and was connected to output bit 1. A 12 V lamp acted as a heater and was connected to output bit 0. An alarm was added to the original design. This was to act as a door-open warning device. The alarm was a 6 V buzzer that was connected to output bit 2. The door sensor was a reed switch on the door and this was connected to input bit 0. The input and output devices are shown in Figure 3.20.

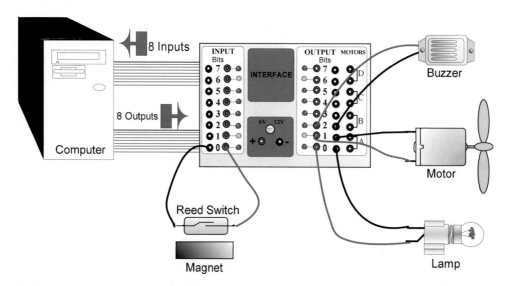

**Figure 3.20** *Connecting the digital input and outputs to the interface*

## Flowchart for the Greenhouse

### Program specification

- Run continuously.
- Continuously monitor the door input sensor. If it is open sound an alarm.
- Continuously monitor the analogue sensor and turn on a heater when the temperature falls below 10° C.
- Continuously monitor the analogue sensor and turn on a cooling fan when the temperature rises above 25° C.

### Program summary

The summary is in three parts:

1. The main program.
2. Down through the cooling fan route.
3. Down through the heater route.

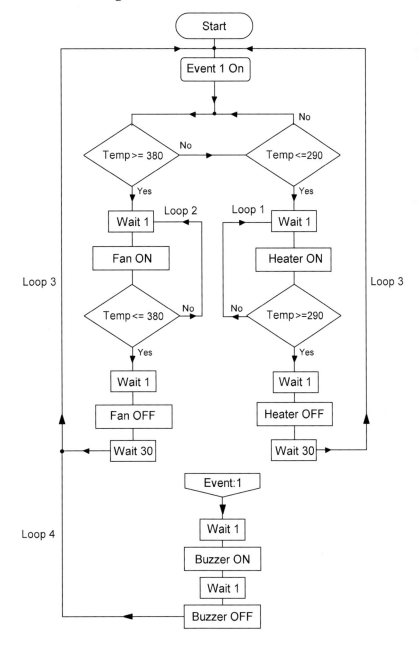

**Figure 3.21** *Flowchart for the computer controlled greenhouse project*

**Flowchart summary for the greenhouse main program**

| Cell name | Program function | Input/output state |
|---|---|---|
| Start | | |
| Event 1 ON | Sub-routine monitoring input 0 | |
| Event:1 | Input Decision | I/P · · · · 1 |
| Wait 1 second | Time loop | |
| Buzzer ON | Output | O/P 0 0 0 0 0 0 0 1 |
| Wait 1 second | Time loop | |
| Buzzer OFF | Output | O/P 0 0 0 0 0 0 0 0 |
| Loop 4 | Goto | |

**Figure 3.22** *Flowchart summary for main program*

**Flowchart summary for the cooling fan**

| Cell Name | Program function | Input/outut state |
|---|---|---|
| Temp>=380 | Analogue input | >=380 |
| Wait 1 second | Time loop | |
| Fan ON | Output | O/P 0 0 0 0 0 0 1 0 |
| Temp<=380 | Analogue input | <=380 |
| Loop 2 | Goto | |
| Wait 30 seconds | Time loop | O/P 0 0 0 0 0 0 0 0 |
| Fan OFF | Output | |
| Loop 3 | Repeat Loop | |

**Figure 3.23** *Flowchart summary for the cooling fan*

**Flowchart summary for the heater**

| Cell Name | Program function | Input/outut state |
|---|---|---|
| Temp<=290 | Analogue input | <=290 |
| Wait 1 second | Time loop | |
| Heater ON | Output | O/P 0 0 0 0 1 0 0 0 |
| Temp<=290 | Analogue input | >=290 |
| Loop 2 | Goto | |
| Wait 30 seconds | Time loop | |
| Fan OFF | Output | O/P 0 0 0 0 0 0 0 0 |
| Loop 3 | Repeat loop | |

**Figure 3.24** *Flowchart summary for the heater*

### Building the circuit

The final design used a purpose built interface circuit housed in a protective box. The circuit for the analogue interface circuit is shown in Figure 3.25. The circuit for the digital interface is shown in Figure 3.26. The PC contained a BBC I/O card. This made the connection to the computer relatively easy as the card has separate ports for output (printer port), input (user port) and analogue (analogue port).

### Analogue interface

The analogue interface used ADVAL 1 from analogue port on the computer. The signal from the analogue port was constantly monitored and used to control the outputs.

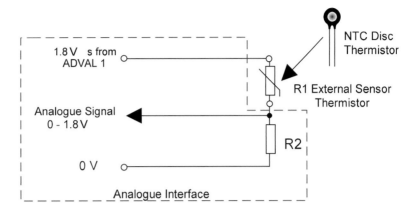

**Figure 3.25** *Circuit diagram for the analogue interface*

### Digital output interface

Output bit 0 was used to control the heater circuit. Output bit 1 was used to control the cooling fan.

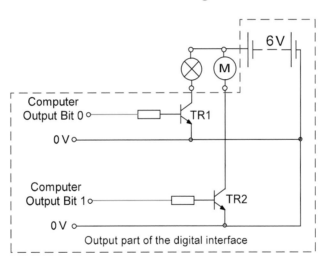

**Figure 3.26** *Circuit diagram for the digital output interface*

### Digital input interface

Input bit 0 was used to detect the condition of the greenhouse door. A reed switch was fitted to the door frame and a magnet to the door. The reed switch contacts were held closed by the magnet. This produced a high signal at input 0. When the door was open the reed switch contacts opened, producing a low signal at input 0. This is shown in Figure 3.27.

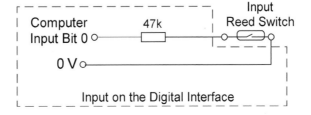

**Figure 3.27** *Circuit diagram for the digital input interface*

# PICs

The term PIC stands for Peripheral Interface Controller. It is an IC that can be programmed to respond to one or more inputs and to control one or more outputs. It is often referred to as a computer-on-a-chip. This is because it enables you to manufacture computer control projects without having to leave your project wired to the computer. You simply download your program to a PIC. The PIC is then plugged into your circuit board. The PIC is a mini programmable processor IC that can be repeatedly programmed and reprogrammed. It has within it all the necessary sub-systems to allow it to do this job.

## Internal structure of the PIC

The PIC will have built-in:

- ROM (Read Only Memory).
- RAM (Random Access Memory).
- I/O (Input Output).
- CPU (Central Processing Unit).

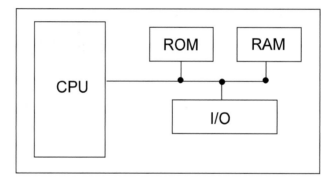

**Figure 3.28** *PIC building blocks*

These are the building blocks of all computers although PCs will have larger and sometimes more of these as well as some others. But basically they are the same.

## PIC types

There are a number of different PICs available for you to purchase and many people will have their favourites but for GCSE project work the following seem to be the most popular:

| PIC Type | Number of pins | I/O pins | Inputs | Outputs |
|---|---|---|---|---|
| PIC12F641 | 8 | 6 | 2 digital | 4 |
| PIC12F675 | 8 | 6 | 2 digital 2 analogue | 2 |
| PIC16F84 | 18 | 13 | 5 digital | 8 |
| PIC16F716 | 18 | 13 | 5 digital 2 analogue | 8 |
| PIC16F873 | 28 | 22 | 8 digital 4 analogue | 8 |
| PIC16F627 | 18 | 15 | 5 digital 2 analogue | 8 |

**Figure 3.29** *PIC 16F84*

Once you have mastered one PIC the rest are much the same. Some will have all digital or all analogue inputs. Others will have a mixture of both, so to simplify things a little the 18pin PIC16F84, the 28 pin PIC16F873 and the PIC 16F627 will be considered in detail to give you a detailed understanding of digital PICs as well as digital and analogue PICs.

### Connecting the PIC 12F641

The PIC12F641 is an eight-pin IC. It requires a stable 6 V supply. Four 1.5 V AA batteries will work fine. This PIC has six input/outputs. All six are input/outputs and bi-directional, that is, they can be made to act as inputs or outputs. Two of the most popular combinations are:

- four outputs, two inputs
- four inputs, two outputs

This PIC has an internal clock, with the simplest construction.

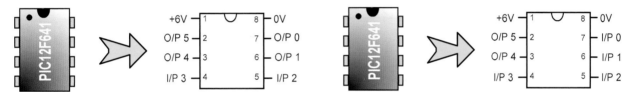

**Figure 3.30** *Combination A*          **Figure 3.31** *Combination B*

#### Connecting the power

Pin 1 = + 6 V. Pin 8 = 0 V. You will also need a decoupling capacitor between pin 1 and 0 V.

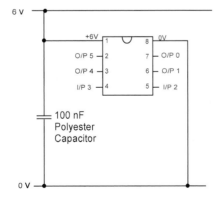

**Figure 3.32** *Power*

#### Connecting the inputs

In this example, pins 4–5 have been set as inputs. You can tie the inputs high or low. This example ties both inputs low through a 10 k resistor. When the push-to-make switch is pressed the input will detect a high.

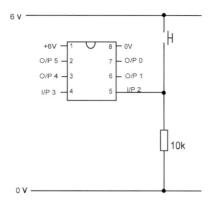

**Figure 3.33** *Inputs*

### Connecting an output

In this example, pins 2, 3, 6 and 7 have been set as outputs. For all but LEDs you will need to amplify the output signal coming from the PIC. This can be achieved simply by using the output signal to turn on a Darlington pair transistor. It is the transistor that drives the output device.

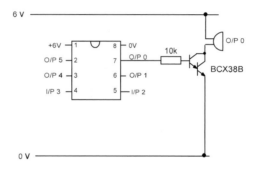

**Figure 3.34** *Outputs*

### Connecting the PIC12F675

The PIC12F675 is an eight-pin IC. It has two digital inputs, two analogue inputs and two outputs. You will need to connect it to a stable 6 V supply. Four 1.5 V AA batteries will be fine for this. The IC has an internal clock so you will not need a resonator.

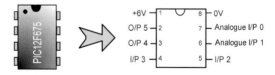

**Figure 3.35** *PIC12F675 pin layout*

### Connecting the power supply

Pin 1 = + 6 V. Pin 8 = 0 V. You will need a 100 nF decoupling capacitor between pin 1 and 0 V. It is also good practice to add a 100 µF electrolytic smoothing capacitor between 6 V and 0 V.

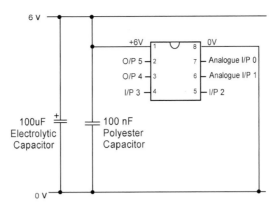

**Figure 3.36** *Connecting the power supply*

### Connecting digital inputs

Pins 4 and 5 are digital inputs 3–2. These can be either tied high or low. In this example they are tied low. When the switch is pressed the PIC will detect a high. It is good practice to tie all unused inputs low.

### Connecting the analogue inputs

The analogue input should come from a potential divider as shown in Figure 3.38.

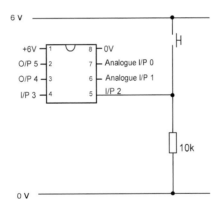

**Figure 3.37** *Connecting digital inputs*

The sensor should be connected to the 6 V positive rail and have a resistance of less than 10 k. The voltage arriving at the analogue input pin can be between 0 and 6 V. The voltage must then be converted into a number of digits. This number will depend on the software or programming language used. Most software packages use 0 – 255. All these packages identify the zero voltage as the number 0 and the 6 V as the number 255.

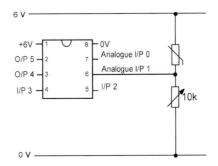

**Figure 3.38** *Analogue inputs*

### Connecting the outputs

Pins 2 and 3 are set as outputs 5–4.

For all but LEDs you will need to amplify the output signal coming from the PIC. This can be achieved simply by using the output signal to turn on a BCX38B Darlington pair transistor. This is shown in Figure 3.39.

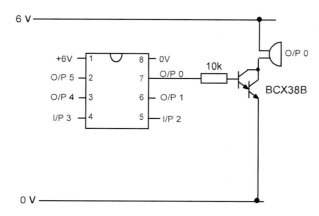

**Figure 3.39** *Adding outputs*

## Connecting the PIC16F84

The PIC16F84 is an 18 pin IC. It has five inputs and eight outputs. You will need to connect it to a stable 6 V supply. Four 1.5 V AA batteries will be fine for this. The IC needs an external clock in the form of a 4 MHz resonator. You will also need to add a reset push-to-make switch to enable you to reset the program.

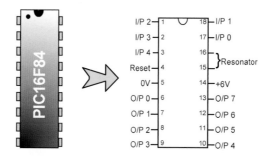

**Figure 3.40** *PIC 16F84 pin layout*

### Connecting the power supply

Pin 14 = + 6 V and pin 5 = 0 V. You will also need a 100 nF decoupling capacitor between pin 14 and 0 V and a100µF smoothing capacitor across the supply.

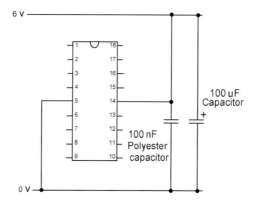

**Figure 3.41** *Power*

### Connecting the reset

Pin 4 = reset. You must keep this high to enable the PIC to work but once the reset switch is pressed the program will reset.

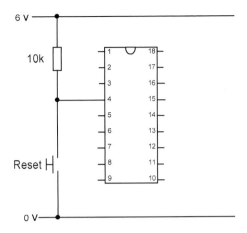

**Figure 3.42** *Reset*

### Connecting the resonator

Pins 15 and 16 are the resonator pins. The third (middle) leg of the three-pin resonator must be connected to 0 V.

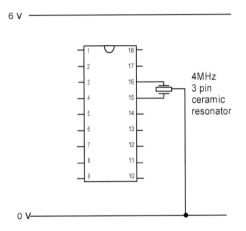

**Figure 3.43** *External clock*

### Connecting the inputs

Pins 1–3 and 17 and 18 are the inputs. You would tie the inputs low, then by using a switch, offer a high to the pin.

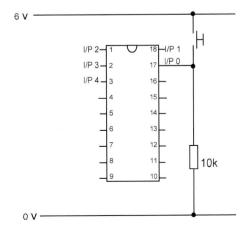

**Figure 3.44** *Inputs*

# PIC16F84

The PIC16F84 has become a very popular choice for Technology and Design students. It has five digital inputs and eight outputs. This makes it ideal for use in projects that require up to five digital inputs and up to eight outputs. Projects such as security systems, combination locks, long timers, event counters, buggies, seven-segment displays, traffic light controllers and many more. A number of these projects will be explained in detail later in this chapter. But first, it is important to come to terms with the chip itself as knowing and understanding this will enable you not only to use the PIC16F84 but also to design, construct and fault-find your circuits. A step-by-step guide to designing a circuit containing the PIC16F84 will now be explained in detail.

## A Step-by-step guide to building a circuit using the PIC16F84

### Graphic symbol

The graphic symbol for the PIC16F84 is shown in Figure 3.45. Each pin is shown as a line with the pin number resting on it.

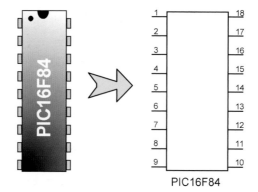

**Figure 3.45** *Symbol for the PIC16F84*

## Step 1: adding the power supply

Connect the positive to pin 14. Next connect the negative to pin 5.

Add a smoothing capacitor C1, between the positive and negative of the supply.

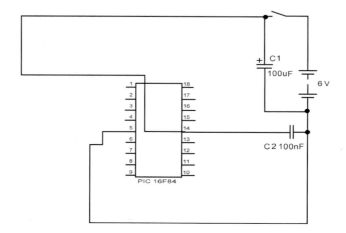

**Figure 3.46** *Adding the power supply to the PIC16F84*

Add a 100 nF decoupling capacitor C2, between the pin 14 and negative. This will ensure the smooth operation of the PIC16F84. This is shown in Figure 3.46.

### Step 2: adding the reset

This is added in two parts. First connect a 10 k resistor between positive and pin 4. This keeps the pin 4 high. Next connect a push-to-make switch between pin 4 and negative, this will enable you to make a low at pin 4. Each time the push-to-make switch is pressed, a low will be present at pin 4. This low will cause the program inside the PIC to reset to the start. This is shown in Figure 3.47.

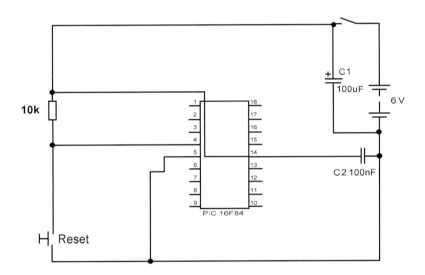

**Figure 3.47** *Adding the reset*

### Step 3: adding the resonator

You will need a 4MHz three-pin resonator. The middle pin is connected to negative. The other two legs are connected to pins

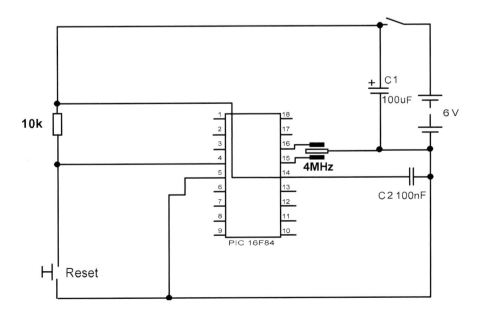

**Figure 3.48** *Adding the resonator*

15 and 16. These legs can be connected either way round. The purpose of the resonator is to provide a clock pulse. The PIC will need this pulse to keep the program working in real time. This is shown in Figure 3.48.

### Step 4: adding an input

You have five digital inputs on the PIC16F84. These are labelled input 0–4. An input is detected by the PIC when the input signal (voltage) changes from low (0) to high (1) or *vice versa*.

### Pull-down resistors

A 10 k pull-down resistor is connected between pin 3 and the negative rail. This is shown in Figure 3.49. The 10 k resistor holds the input low until you press the push-to-make switch. When the input is pressed the signal appearing at pin 3 goes high. You can then write a program that will incorporate this change from low to high (from 0 to 1).

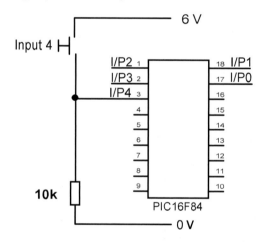

**Figure 3.49**

*Connecting inputs*

### Inputs 0–4

It is good practice to pull all the inputs either high or low even if they are not being used. This will help prevent false signals appearing at the pins. The circuit shown in Figure 3.50 uses only one input but the other four are pulled low. The following table shows the input pins and their corresponding bit numbers.

**Table 12** *Input pin numbers for the PIC16F84*

| Pin No | 17 | 18 | 1 | 2 | 3 |
|---|---|---|---|---|---|
| Input No | 0 | 1 | 2 | 3 | 4 |

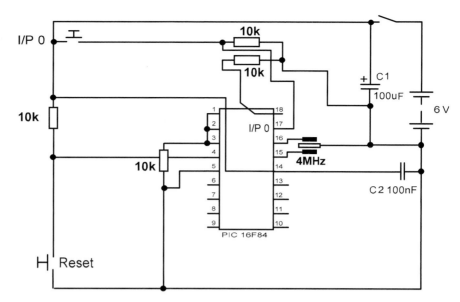

**Figure 3.50** *Connecting the inputs*

## Step 5: adding outputs

The PIC16F84 has eight outputs and you can use one or all as required.

The output pins and the corresponding bit numbers are shown in table 13.

**Table 13** *Output pin numbers for the PIC 16F84*

| Pin No | 6 | 7 | 8 | 9 | 10 | 11 | 12 | 13 |
|---|---|---|---|---|---|---|---|---|
| Output No | 0 | 1 | 2 | 3 | 4 | 5 | 6 | O/P 7 |

The PIC is like any other IC in that the output voltage will be close to the supply voltage but the current will be low. This small current is only suitable for low-current devices such as LEDs. For all other output devices such as relays, lamps and buzzers, you will need to amplify the current.

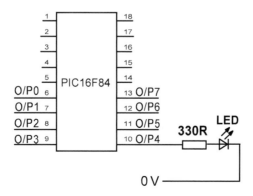

**Figure 3.51** *Adding an output*

### Amplifying an output

The most effective way to amplify the output signal from the PIC16F84 is through a transistor or even better through a Darlington pair transistor. A good low cost Darlington pair transistor is the BCX38B. Connecting a Darlington pair to an output is shown in Figure 3.52.

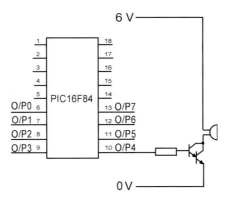

**Figure 3.52** *Amplifying the output signal*

### How it works

The output was required to drive a 6 V buzzer. The buzzer was connected to the 6 V supply rail. An output from pin 10 (output bit 4) is offered to the base leg of the Darlington pair transistor. When this happens, the transistor is on and the larger current from the supply rail can flow through it and the buzzer. This will cause the buzzer to sound. The Darlington pair transistor requires a protective resistor. This can be any value between 1 and 10 k.

### Step 6 Adding outputs to the circuit

The circuit diagram for the PIC16F84 using one input and one output is shown in Figure 3.53. The output is an LED and is connected to output 0 (pin 6).

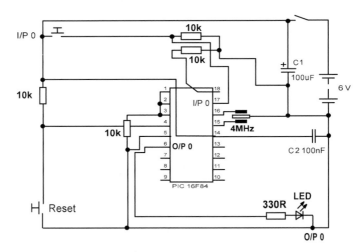

**Figure 3.53** *Connecting an LED to output 0*

### Adding a LED and buzzer to the circuit

The circuit diagram shown in Figure 3.54 incorporates one input and two outputs. The LED and its series resistor are connected directly to the output at pin 6. However, the buzzer is connected to a Darlington pair transistor and draws its current directly from the 6 V power supply.

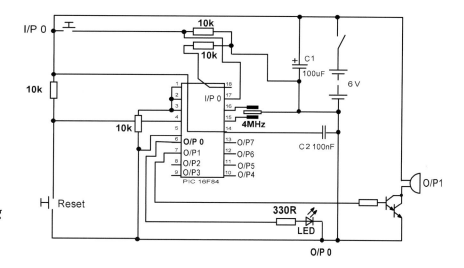

**Figure 3.54** *Connecting an LED and buzzer to outputs 0 and 1*

## Using the PIC to drive motors and solenoids

If you wish to use the PIC to drive motors, solenoids or other similar electromotive devices it will be necessary to use a relay. This should avoid many of the problems associated with false signals getting back to the PIC. These problems are often intermittent but can cause your PIC to malfunction. By isolating these devices through a relay and using a secondary power supply your project should work correctly. If you are using a relay you should connect a diode across the coil of the relay to allow for back e.m.f (electromotive force).

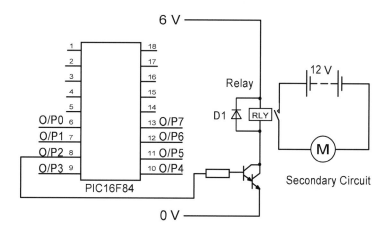

**Figure 3.55** *Using motors with the PIC16F84*

## PIC16F84 circuit incorporating a secondary circuit

A secondary circuit operated by the relay is shown in Figure 3.56. The relay will come on when output 2 goes high. The type of relay used with the PIC will also be important. Miniature relays that pull the contacts down onto the coil can often give problems such as false signals. From experience it was found that the *Finder DPDT 5A 40.52* relays gave the best results.

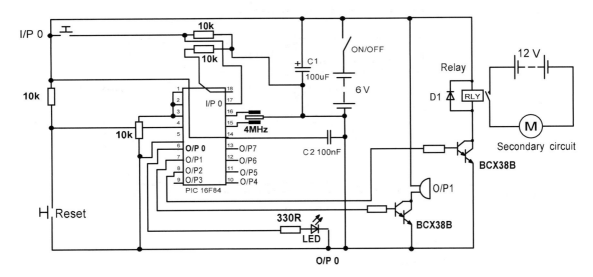

**Figure 3.56** *PIC16F84 incorporating a secondary circuit*

## Designing a circuit using two inputs and one output

### Design situation

The game of chess requires the player to make a move within a certain period of time. There is a need for a precise timer that would be set by the player once they had completed their move. The opposing player would then have until the light and buzzer came on to complete their move.

### *Solution*

The solution incorporated the PIC16F84. The circuit used two inputs and one output on the PIC16F84. The output is to a BCX38B that is used to turn on the LED and the buzzer, but these could be changed for any other suitable output device.

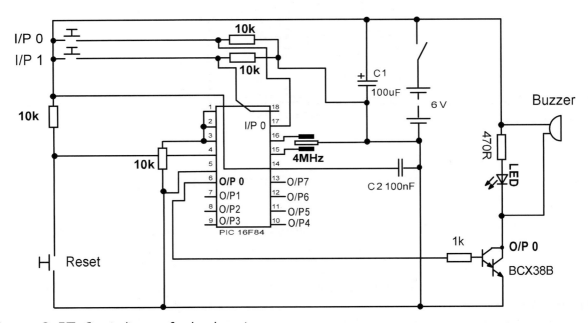

**Figure 3.57** *Circuit diagram for the chess timer*

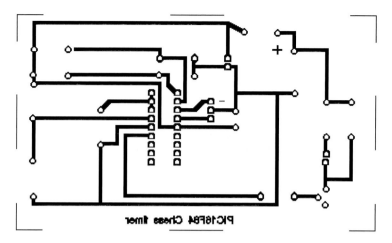

**Figure 3.58** *PCB for the chess timer*

### Bill of materials

1 × PIC16F84
1 × 18 pin DIL socket
1 × 100 µF electrolytic capacitor
1 × 100 nF capacitor
1 × 470 ohms resistor
1 × 4 MHz 3 pin ceramic resonator
4 × 10 k resistors
1 × 1 k resistor
1 × BCX38B transistor
1 × green LED
1 × 6 volt buzzer
2 × push-to-make switch
1 × SPST toggle switch
1 × board 106.5mm × 68.5mm

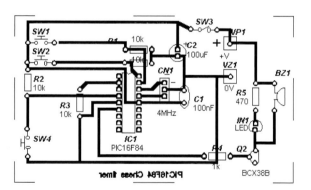

**Figure 3.59** *Silk screen for the chess timer*

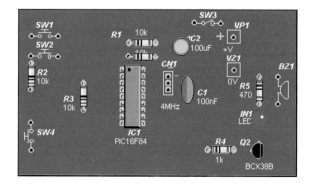

**Figure 3.60** *Top view of the chess timer PCB*

## Program sequence for chess timer

- Start.
- LED and buzzer off.
- Press switch 1 to start the game.
- Wait for two minutes for the player to make a move or check whether the reset switch has been pressed. If yes, go to start. If no, go to next line.
- LED and buzzer on and off every 0.5 seconds until switch 2 is pressed.
- Press switch 2 to return to start.

### Flowchart for chess timer

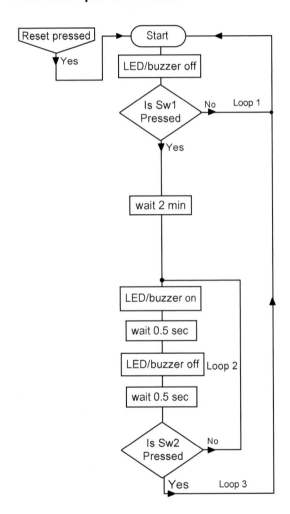

**Figure 3.61** *Flowchart for the chess timer*

## Flowchart summary

| Cell name | Program function | Input/output state |
|---|---|---|
| Start | | |
| LED/buzzer off | Output | O/P 0 0 0 0 0 0 0 0 |
| Loop 1 | GOTO start | |
| Is SW1 pressed? | Input decision | I/P ... 0 1 |
| Wait 120 seconds | Time loop | |
| Is reset pressed? | GOTO state (event) | |
| LED/buzzer on | Output | O/P 0 0 0 0 0 0 0 1 |
| Wait 0.5 seconds | Time loop | |
| LED/buzzer off | Output | O/P 0 0 0 0 0 0 0 0 |
| Wait 0.5 seconds | Time loop | |
| Is SW2 pressed? | Input decision | I/P ... 1 0 |
| Loop 2 | GOTO | |
| Loop 3 | Repeat Loop | |

**Figure 3.62** *Summary for chess timer program*

## Example    PIC16F84 Target project

### Design situation

A local fairground has a shooting gallery. They need a display that would tell the stallholder when a target was hit and also display its value. The value had to be added to the total score each time.

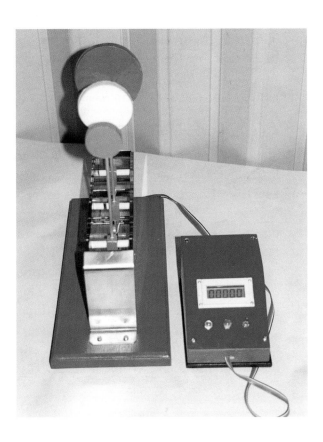

**Figure 3.63** *Picture of the target*

### Solution

The solution had three targets increasing in size. Each was connected to an input switch. The PIC16F84 was chosen as the microprocessor for the circuit and an LCD display as the output device. The LCD selected had a reset so that the display could be reset to zero after each customer.

## Circuit diagram for the target

The circuit was based on the standard PIC16F84 circuit diagram shown in Figure 3.53. The final modified circuit is shown in Figure 3.64.

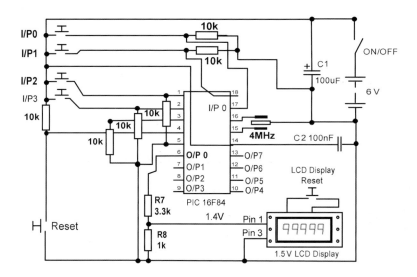

**Figure 3.64** *Circuit diagram for the target-counter*

### Inputs

The final circuit used four of the five inputs with the unused input being tied low through a 10 k resistor. Each input was connected to a micro-switch. When the target arm was pushed back with the pellet, it activated the micro-switch.

### Output LCD counter module

This project incorporated an LCD counter module that has an internal 1.5 V power supply. Interfacing the output from the PIC16F84 to the module was a simple matter of pulsing pin 3 on the module. This was achieved by first removing the front panel on the module to expose soldering terminals numbered 1–7. The output voltage from bit 0 on the PIC16F84 was 6 V and had to be reduced through a potential divider to just less than 1.5 V before connecting it to pin 3 on the LCD. The potential divider used in the circuit is shown in Figure 3.66. Finally, the negative on the module was connected to the negative on the PIC board. Connecting a push-to-make switch between pins 2 and 4 on the module made the reset for the LCD counter.

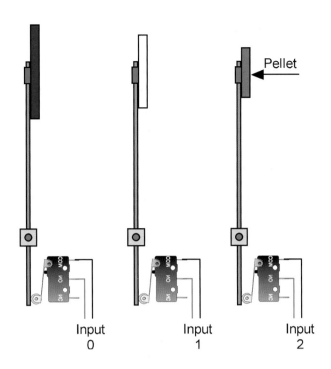

**Figure 3.65** *Target micro-switches*

Input 0     Input 1     Input 2

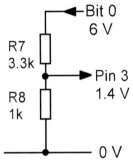

**Figure 3.66** *Potential divider circuit*

## Potential divider circuit

Calculating the voltage drop across R8

$$R8 = \frac{R8}{R7 + R8} \times 6\,V$$

$$R8 = \frac{1 \times 6}{1 + 3.3} = \frac{6}{4.3} = 1.395$$

$$R8 = 1.395 \text{ or } 1.4\,V$$

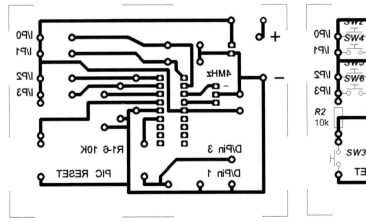

**Figure 3.67** *Target PCB*

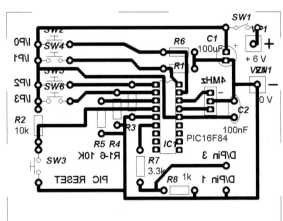

**Figure 3.68** *Target silk screen*

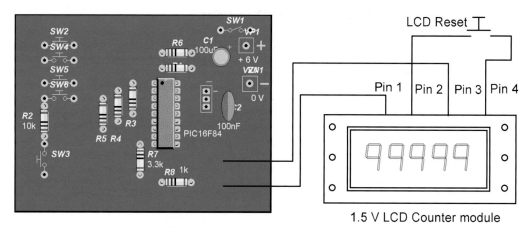

**Figure 3.69** *Top view of the target PCB*

### Program design sequence for target counter

Each contestant purchases five pellets. Before each pellet is fired, 'start game' is pressed. After all the pellets have been fired the LCD reset can be pressed to reset the display. Pressing the PIC reset resets the program. The flowchart for the program is shown in Figure 3.69.

#### Program details

- Start.
- Press 'start game' for next shot.
- Loop 2.
- Fire: If target 1 hit pulse 1; if target 2 hit, pulse 2; if target 3 hit, pulse 3 (note: each pulse causes the LCD to add one to the last count).
- Wait for 0.5 second.
- Go round loop 3, 4 or 5 until $\times$ = to 1, 2 or 3.
- Return to start via loop 6.
- Press PIC reset switch to cancel the score and start a new game.

#### Summary for target counter

| Cell name | Program function | Input/output state |
|---|---|---|
| Start | | |
| Loop 1 | GOTO | |
| Start game pressed | Input decision | I/P · I · · · |
| Loop 2 | GOTO | |
| Target 1 hit | Input decision | I/P · · · · I |
| Loop 3 then loop 6 | GOTO | |
| Target 2 hit | Input decision | I/P · · · I |
| Loop 4 then loop 6 | GOTO | |
| Target 3 hit | Input decision | I/P · · I |
| Loop 5 then loop 6 | GOTO | |

**Figure 3.70** Summary for the main program

## Flowchart for target counter

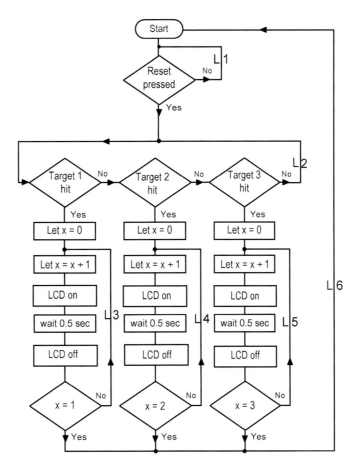

**Figure 3.71** *Flowchart for target counter*

The next part of the summary has three possible paths depending on which target is hit e.g. path 1 when target 1 hit.

| Let $x = 0$ | Set $x$ as a variable | |
| Let $x = x + 1$ | Add 1 to the value of $x$ | |
| LCD on | Output | O/P 0 0 0 0 0 0 0 1 |
| Wait 0.5 seconds | Time loop1 | |
| LCD off | Output | O/P 0 0 0 0 0 0 0 0 |
| $x = 1*$ | Compare/decision | |
| Loop 3 or Loop 6 | GOTO | |

* All the paths are the same except for the one line: $x =$. The value 1–3 would be changed on this line. The paths are shown in Figure 3.71.

**Figure 3.72** *Flowchart summary*

# Commercial software for programming the PIC

There are a number of very good software packages you can purchase that will help you program and enable you to download these programs to the PIC. Two of the most popular packages are PIC-Logicator and PICAXE. It is also possible to purchase software that will allow you to program completely in BASIC or ladder logic. PICAXE software has the added advantage that it will convert your flowchart program into BASIC at the click of a button on your computer.

At present PIC-Logicator and PICAXE are the most commonly used in software package for schools and will be used in the next few design solution.

    **Golf putting practice mat**

### Design situation

Putting is an import part of golf and it is important to practise this skill. There is a need for an indoor putting mat that will have a level of difficulty built in.

### Solution

A golf putting practice mat that used the same PIC16F84 circuit designed for the target counter shown in figure 3.64. The game incorporates four input micro-switches. One at the bottom of each of the three holes in the plastic pipe on the putting mat and a fourth starts the game.

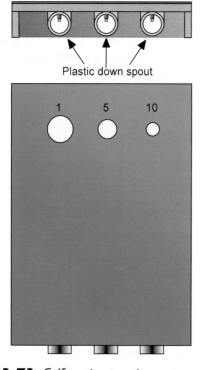

**Figure 3.73** *Golf putting practice mat*

**Figure 3.74** *LCD display module made for the golf putting practice mat*

The plastic pipe is also used to return the ball. The three holes were of different sizes. A ball going down the smaller hole gains 10 points. The middle hole 5 points and the larger hole 1 point. As the ball fell into the holes a micro-switch was pressed and the LCD counter was programmed to show a numerical score. Commercial software and programming board was used to program the PIC.

## Programming the PIC16F84 used in the golf putting practice mat using PIC-Logicator software

In PIC-Logicator you simply draw the flowchart, as you want the program to function. The cells in the flowchart perform specific operations. These are listed below.

- GAME START is an input decision in which the program moves back to start until input bit 4 goes high (1). At this point the program moves to the next cell.
- The program moves around the three-point decision cells until the golf ball hits one of the micro-switches giving a high signal. When this happens, the program moves down that specific line in the flowchart.
- If it moves down the 1 point line, the count A (variable) is set to zero before the program jumps out of the main program to do the macro 'COUNT ONE'.
- 'COUNT ONE' turns on output bit 0 for half a second before turning it off and ending the macro. At this point the program jumps back into the main program which sends it around to the start again. This pulse at Bit0 causes the LCD counter to advance its count by one.
- If the program moves down the 5 or 10 points lines in the flowchart the program completes the macro 5 or 10 times before returning to the start. This pulse at Bit0 causes the LCD counter to advance by 5 or 10.

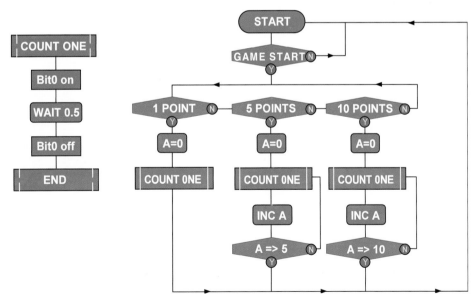

**Figure 3.75** *PIC-Logicator flowchart for the golf putting practice mat*

### Summary of PIC-Logicator flowchart

| Port Decision | Game start | . . . . 1 . . . |
|---|---|---|
| | 1 Point | . . . . . . . 1 |
| | 5 Points | . . . . . . 1 . |

**147**

|  | 10 Points | . . . . . 1 . . |
|---|---|---|
| Port output functions | Bit0 on | 0 0 0 0 0 0 0 1 |
|  | Bit0 off | 0 0 0 0 0 0 0 0 |
| Macros | COUNT ONE | |

---

**Example**     **PIC16F84 Event Counter**

### Design Situation

During football training sessions, one of the exercises is to run down the gym, touch the back wall and run back up again. This exercise has to be repeated ten times.

### Solution

The PIC16F84 was used to count the number of times the player reached the back wall. The PIC had a push-to-make switch that was fixed to the wall to act as an input. The output device was a seven-segment display. Each time the input was detected, the PIC increased the count by one.

**Figure 3.76** *Event counter*

## PIC16F84 Event counter circuit diagram

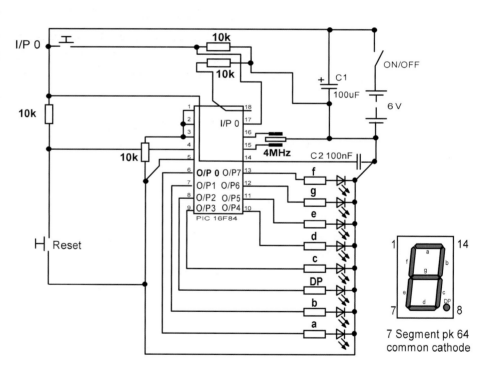

**Figure 3.77** *PIC16F84 Event counter circuit diagram*

# PCB Details for the PIC16F84 Event counter

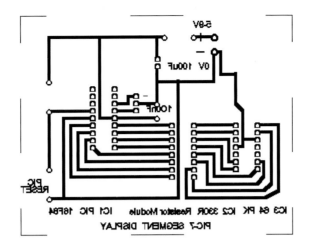

**Figure 3.78** *Event counter PCB*

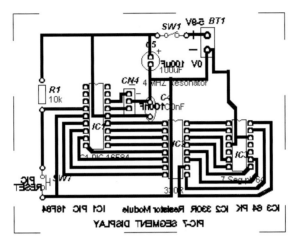

**Figure 3.79** *Event counter silk screen*

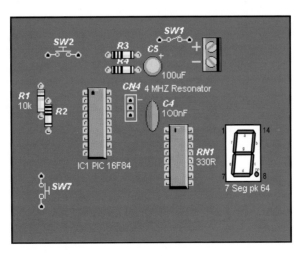

**Figure 3.80** *Top view of the event counter PCB*

## Bill of materials

2 × push-to-make switches
1 × 330 ohms resistor IC
1 × 7 segment display common cathode pk 70
1 × PIC16F84
1 × 18 pin DIL socket
1 × 16 pin DIL socket
1 × 14 pin DIL socket

1 × 4MHz 3-pin ceramic resonator

1 × 100 μF capacitor

1 × 100 nF capacitor

4 × 10 k resistors

1 × board 84 mm × 66 mm

### Program sequence for the Event counter

- Start.
- If switch is pressed display the number 1.
- If switch is pressed display the number 2.
- If switch is pressed display the number 3.
- If switch is pressed display the number 4.
- If switch is pressed display the number 5.
- If switch is pressed display the number 6.
- If switch is pressed display the number 7.
- If switch is pressed display the number 8.
- If switch is pressed display the number 9.
- Wait for 10 seconds.
- Display the number 0.
- Go to start.

## Programming the PIC16F84 used in the event counter using PIC-Logicator software

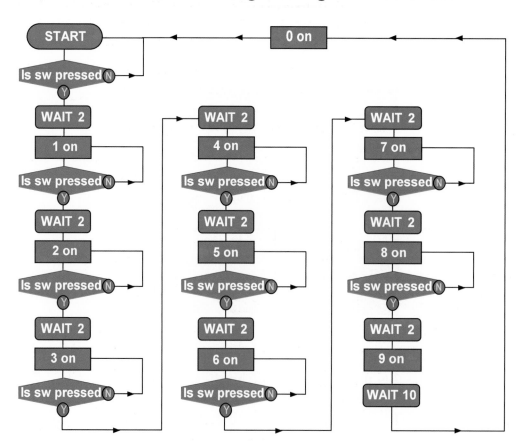

**Figure 3.81** *Event counter PIC-Logicator flowchart*

## Summary of PIC-Logicator flowchart for the event counter

Start

| | | | |
|---|---|---|---|
| Port decision | | Is SW pressed? . . . . . . . 1 | |
| Port output functions | 1 on | 0 0 0 0 1 0 1 0 | |
| | 2 on | 0 1 1 1 0 0 1 1 | |
| | 3 on | 0 1 0 1 1 0 1 1 | |
| | 4 on | 1 1 0 0 1 0 1 0 | |
| | 5 on | 1 1 0 1 1 0 0 1 | |
| | 6 on | 1 1 1 1 1 0 0 0 | |
| | 7 on | 0 0 0 0 1 0 1 1 | |
| | 8 on | 1 1 1 1 1 0 1 1 | |
| | 9 on | 1 1 0 0 1 0 1 1 | |
| | 0 on | 1 0 1 1 1 0 1 1 | |

---

| Example | PIC16F84 Alarm System |
|---|---|

### Design situation

After a number of burglaries in the area there was a need for an alarm system to protect the home.

### Solution

The solution incorporated a PIC16F84 that was programmed to detect any one of five inputs. The circuit uses two relays, one to drive a bell and the other to drive a strobe light.

The third output is a status LED to indicate the program's running. The circuit is shown in Figure 3.82.

## Specification for the alarm program

- The alarm is set using a key switch and an LED comes on.
- The occupants should have 30 seconds to leave the building, after which time the alarm will be armed.

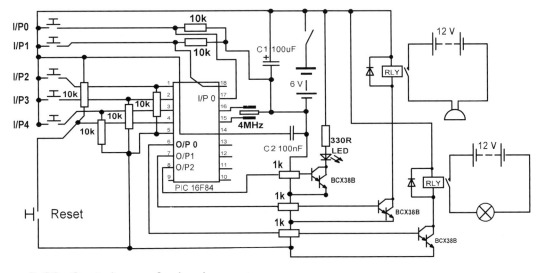

**Figure 3.82** *Circuit diagram for the alarm system*

- Each of the three downstairs doors should have a sensor that will trigger the alarm after a 30 second delay.
- On re-entry the alarm will be activated. There should be a 30 second delay to allow for the alarm to be reset before it is activated.
- If more than 30 seconds has passed and the alarm has not been reset, the bell should sound and the strobe light should flash.
- After 20 minutes the bell should stop but the strobe should continue until the alarm is reset with the key.

### Additional feature:

- At any point after the alarm is set or activated, the key switch should reset it. When using PIC-Logicator this is possible by using a command called an event. The event has three elements to it.

1. Event on: the point in the program you want the event to come on
2. Event off: the point in the program you want the event to go off
3. The event itself. This is an input decision and must include the point in the program you want the event to go to when it has happened.

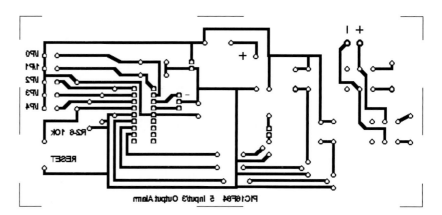

**Figure 3.83** *PCB for PIC16F84 alarm system*

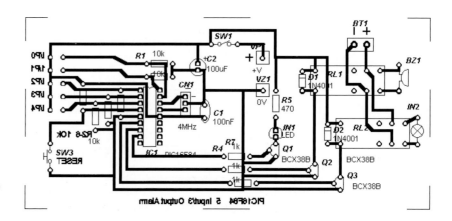

**Figure 3.84** *Silk screen for PIC16F84 alarm system*

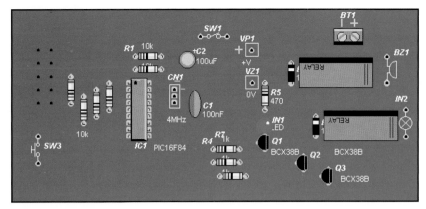

**Figure 3.85** *Top view of the alarm PCB*

### Bill of materials

1 × PIC16F84
1 × 18 pin DIL socket
1 × 100 nF capacitor
1 × 100 µF capacitor
1 × 330 ohms resistor
1 × 4 MHz 3 pin ceramic resonator
5 × 10 k resistors
3 × 1 k resistor
3 × BCX38B transistor
1 × green LED
5 × push-to-make switches
1 × key switch
1 × SPST toggle switch
1 × 12 V Bell
1 × 12 V Strobe light
1 × board 160 mm × 73.5 mm

## Alarm flowchart

This flowchart shows the alarm program with the event included. If you plan to use the event then you can delete the last three decisions (Key SW0 off). If you are not using the event then delete it and its elements (EVENT 1, ON and EVENT 1, OFF). This is shown in Figure 3.86.

### Summary of PIC-Logicator flowchart for the alarm

| | | |
|---|---|---|
| Start | | |
| Port decision | Key SW0 on | . . . . . . . 1 |
| | Key SW0 off | . . . . . . . 0 |
| | is SW1 pressed | . . . . . . 1 . |
| | is SW2 pressed | . . . . . 1 . . |
| | is SW3 pressed | . . . . 1 . . . |
| Events | 1:Key SW0 off | . . . . . . . 0 |
| Port output functions | LED on | 0 0 0 0 0 1 0 0 |
| | S+B on | 0 0 0 0 0 1 1 1 |
| | S on | 0 0 0 0 0 1 0 1 |
| | Alarm off | 0 0 0 0 0 0 0 0 |

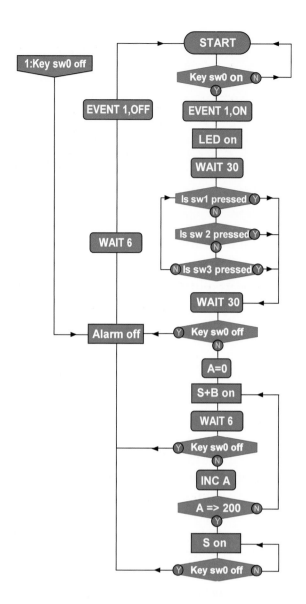

**Figure 3.86** *Flowchart for the alarm project*

## Connecting low-voltage d.c. motors to the PIC16F84

The PIC16F84 can be connected to a L293D low-voltage motor driver IC. A d.c. motor can be connected to the IC across pins 3 and 4. If you want your motor to run forward and backwards you can connect it across two out pins such as 3 and 6. This is shown in Figure 3.87.

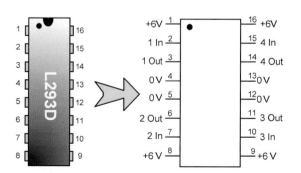

**Figure 3.87** *L293D Motor driver IC*

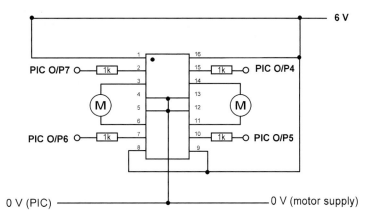

**Figure 3.88** *Circuit diagram for the L293D*

## How it works

### Single motor forward only

When you send a high signal to an input (In) pin this allows the supply voltage and 1 amp of current to flow out of the matching output (Out) pin. By connecting a d.c. motor between the output pin and 0 volts, the motor will turn in a forward rotation for as long as the input pin is high.

### Single motor forward and reverse

You can make your motor rotate forwards and in reverse by connecting it across two output pins. This enables the current to flow out of one output and into the other before flowing to 0 volts through the IC. For example, a motor is connected as shown in Figure 3.88, then when pin 2 is on (high), current will flow out of output pin 3 through the motor and into pin 6 causing the motor to rotate clockwise. If input pin 2 is off and input pin 7 on, the current will flow out of pin 6 through the motor into pin 3 making the motor rotate in an anti-clockwise direction.

## Connecting two motors

The advantage of using the L293D is that two motors can be connected to the IC. These can also be made to turn forwards and in reverse. This will allow you to use the L293D with microprocessor-controlled buggies. The pin sequence for the two motors is shown in Figure 3.89.

| Motor | Pin 7 | Pin 2 | Direction | Motor | Pin 15 | Pin 10 | Direction |
|-------|-------|-------|-----------|-------|--------|--------|-----------|
| 1 | High | Low | Forward | 2 | High | Low | Forward |
|  | Low | High | Reverse |  | Low | High | Reverse |

**Figure 3.89** *Controlling two motors*

## Motor voltage

If you wish to use a higher or lower voltage d.c. motor, you must have a separate d.c. power supply to suit the motor. Remember to connect negative from both power supplies together or the circuit will not work. This is shown in Figure 3.88.

### Circuit diagram for the L293D controlled by the PIC16F84

The L293D motor driver IC connected to the PIC16F84 is shown in Figure 3.90. This board was designed to control a buggy that would move forwards and backwards. Two limit switches mounted on the bumper of the buggy where connected to the inputs of the PIC. When the buggy ran into an object, the program detected the input and made the buggy go into reverse, turn, and go forward again.

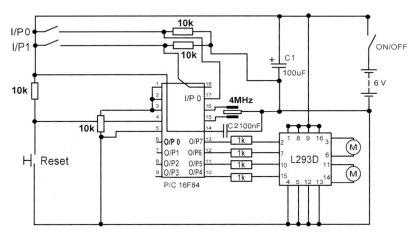

**Figure 3.90** *Circuit diagram for the buggy incorporating the PIC16F84 and L293D*

### Programming the PIC to control the L293D

By connecting outputs 4–7 on the PIC to the L293D you can use the PIC to control the direction of motors 1 and 2. The circuit diagram in Figure 3.89 shows the connection between the PIC16F84 outputs and the L293D inputs.

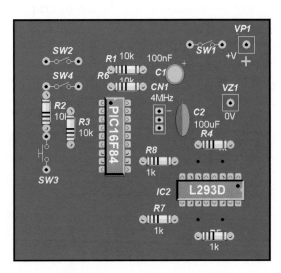

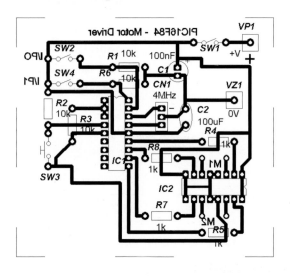

**Figure 3.91** *Top view of the buggy PCB*          **Figure 3.92** *PCB for the PIC16F84-L293D*

### Bill of Materials

1 × PIC16F84
1 × 18 pin DIL socket
1 × 16 pin DIL socket
1 × 100 nF capacitor
1 × 100 µF capacitor
5 × 10 k resistors
3 × 1 k resistor
4 × 10 k resistors
1 × 4 MHz 3 pin ceramic resonator
4 × 1 k resistors
2 × Micro switches
1 × SPST toggle switch
1 × board 81 mm × 73.5 mm
1 × L293D motor driver IC

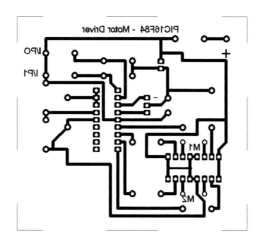

**Figure 3.93** *Silk screen PIC16F84-L293D*

## Using the PIC16F84 to turn on multiple outputs

### Turning on one output device

The PIC16F84 is only capable of an output current of 50 mA. This is too little current to turn on any output device other than an LED. Therefore it will be necessary to use a transistor or, better still, a Darlington pair transistor such as the BCX38B to amplify the output current from the PIC. The BCX38B is designed to allow 800 mA to pass through it safely. This will enable you to drive other larger current devices such as lamps, relays, motors and buzzers. The circuit for this is shown in Figure 3.94.

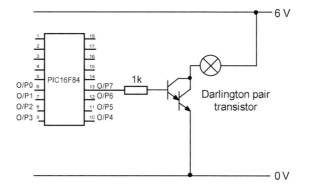

**Figure 3.94** *Amplifying the output signal*

### Turning on a number of output devices

Designing a circuit to turn on a number of output devices can become very complex. This is due to the number of transistor and resistors you are trying to fit unto your board. This can be seen in Figure 3.95

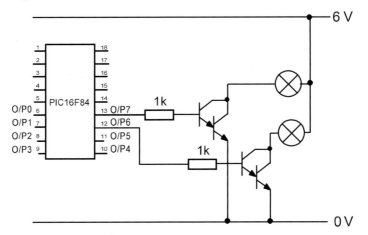

**Figure 3.95** *Amplifying two output signals*

# ULN2803A Darlington pairs IC

You can purchase a UNL2803A Darlington driver IC that will allow you to connect up to eight output devices to your PIC. This IC has eight Darlington pair transistors built-in. The IC is shown in Figure 3.96.

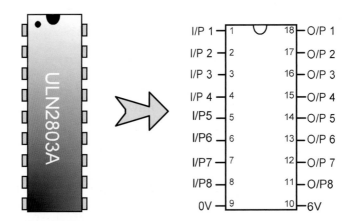

**Figure 3.96**
*ULN2803A Darlington driver IC*

## How the UNL2803A works

When a voltage greater than 1.3 V is present at the base leg of the Darlington pair, a larger voltage and current can flow into the collector and out of the emitter. This is shown in Figure 3.97. The connection through one Darlington pair transistor inside the IC is shown in Figure 3.99. An input at one side of the IC causes the opposite pin to come on. Each transistor has a built-in protective diode at the collector leg. This is to protect the circuit against back e.m.f from electromotive devices such as relays and motors. A drawing of the ULN2803A is show in Figure 3.99.

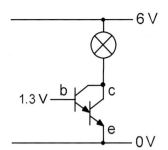

**Figure 3.97** *Switching on the Darlington pair*

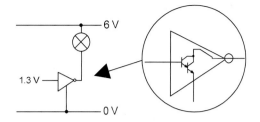

**Figure 3.98** *Darlington pair symbol when used in an IC*

## Connecting the ULN2803A to the PIC16F84

The connection of the ULN2803A to the PIC is a simple matter of making a direct connection from the output pin of the PIC to the input pin of the IC. The connections are straight across. This is shown in Figure 3.100. It is important to remember that each Darlington pair will sink the current appearing at its collector when it detects a voltage greater than 1.3 V at its base. It is a common mistake to think that a high signal at the base pin of the ULN2803A will give out a high signal at the opposite pin. This is not true. A high signal at the base pin will turn on the ULN2803A Darlington pair, allowing the current present at its collector to pass through it and out of the common emitter (pin 9) labelled 0 volts.

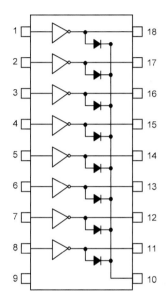

**Figure 3.99** *Inside the ULN2803A*

**Figure 3.100**

*Connecting the ULN2803A to the PIC16F84*

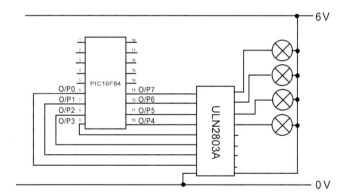

## Using the PIC16F84 to drive stepper motors

Standard d.c. motors turn when you connect the power supply to them and stop when you turn it off. Stepper motors are not like that. They are d.c. motors that move part of a revolution each time you pulse in the four coils that make up the motor correct sequence. The most commonly used stepper motor in schools requires 48-steps or pulses to make it turn through one revolution. This means that each pulse rotates the stepper motor's spindle just 7.5°. The unipolar 48-step stepper motors are the easiest to work with and will be used with the PIC16F84 in this chapter.

There are a number of suppliers of these motors. You will need a 4-pole unipolar stepper motor for connecting to the PIC. TEP's EW2017 was found to be suitable as was Rapid electronics

4-phase unipolar stepper motor. Stepper motors are expensive compared to small d.c. motors, but both of these are good value for money and are suitable for school projects.

## Unipolar stepper motors

These have four pairs of coils fixed around a rotor. When each pair is turned on in the correct sequence, the permanent magnet rotor moves one step. Only two coils are shown in figures 3.101 and 2, there would be four in a stepper motor.

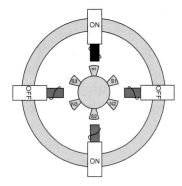

**Figure 3.101** *First pulse*

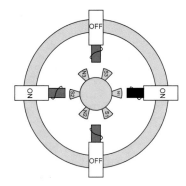

**Figure 3.102** *Second pulse*

These unipolar stepper motors with a common positive, supply four coils. When the current is allowed to flow through a pair of coils in the correct sequence, this causes the magnet to move to the new coil by one step. By pulsing in the correct sequence, it is also possible to rotate the magnetic rotor either clockwise or anticlockwise.

### Making the stepper motor rotate clockwise

|        | Coil 1 | Coil 2 | Coil 3 | Coil 4 |
|--------|--------|--------|--------|--------|
| Step 1 | on     | off    | off    | on     |
| Step 2 | on     | off    | on     | off    |
| Step 3 | off    | on     | on     | off    |
| Step 4 | off    | on     | off    | on     |

**Figure 3.103** *Clockwise rotations*

### Making the stepper motor rotate anticlockwise

|        | Coil 1 | Coil 2 | Coil 3 | Coil 4 |
|--------|--------|--------|--------|--------|
| Step 1 | off    | on     | on     | off    |
| Step 2 | on     | off    | on     | off    |
| Step 3 | on     | off    | off    | on     |
| Step 4 | off    | on     | off    | on     |

**Figure 3.104** *Anticlockwise rotations*

The frequency of the pulses will determine the rotational speed of the stepper motor. The PIC is ideal for controlling the sequence and frequency of these pulses.

### Wiring for the TEP stepper motor coils

The position of the Darlington pair transistors below the coil and the common supply is shown in figure 3.105. The supply voltage of most stepper motors will be 12 V while the PIC will run on 5–6 V. If this is the case, you will need a separate power supply for the stepper motor. Be sure to connect the negatives from both power supplies together or the circuit will not work.

### Coil colour coding for the TEP stepper motor wiring

- Coil 1 Red
- Coil 2 brown
- Coil 3 yellow
- Coil 4 blue
- 0 volts white.

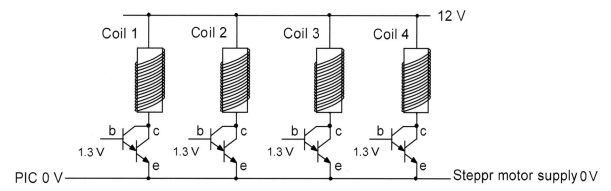

**Figure 3.105** *Stepper motor coil wiring colour codes*

## Using the ULN2803A to drive a stepper motor

The ULN2803A is ideal for driving the stepper motor controlled by the PIC16F84. Each Darlington pair in the IC is capable of sinking 550 mA, which should be sufficient for most stepper motors. However, some stepper motors require 900 mA. In this case it is possible to link two inputs and two outputs on the ULN2803A in pairs to give you 1.1 amps. This is shown in Figure 3.106.

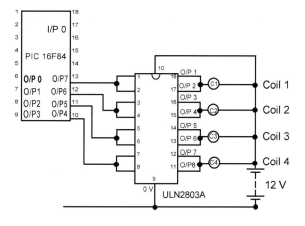

**Figure 3.106**

*Connecting ULN2803A inputs and outputs to give 1.1 amps*

The circuit diagram shown in Figure 3.107 was designed to drive a simple buggy. The buggy had one stepper motor that turned a rear axle. It was designed to run forward until it hit an object, then go into reverse. Micro-switches were positioned at the front and rear of the buggy and acted as input sensors for the PIC program.

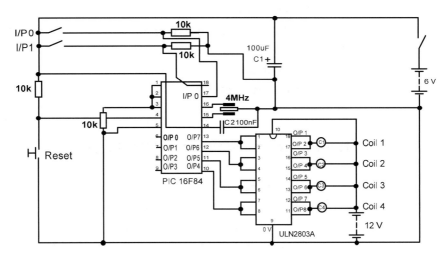

**Figure 3.107** *Circuit diagram for controlling a stepper motor*

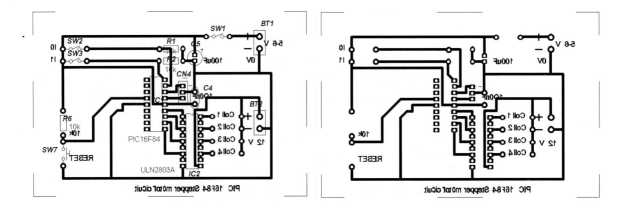

**Figure 3.108** *PCB for the stepper motor*          **Figure 3.109** *Silk screen for the stepper motor*

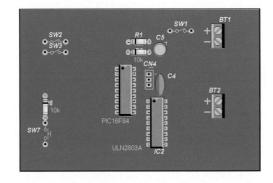

**Figure 3.110** *Top view of the stepper motor PCB*

### Bill of materials

1 × PIC16F84
1 × ULN2803A
2 × 18 pin DIL socket
1 × 100 nF capacitor
1 × 100 µF capacitor
2 × 10 k resistors
1 × 4 MHz 3 pin ceramic resonator
2 × 1 k resistors
2 × micro-switches
1 × SPST toggle switch
1 × board 116 mm × 76.5 mm

## Program sequence for the stepper motor buggy

- Start.
- If input switch 0 and 1 are off, move forward.
- Keep moving forward until input switch 0 is pressed.
- If input switch is pressed, move backwards.
- Keep moving backwards until input switch 1 is pressed.
- If input switch 1 is pressed, move forward.
- Go back to the start.
- One complete revolution of the stepper motor should take 0.4 seconds.

The program has a simple main program with seven cells that contain the input decisions and macros. The control of the stepper motor is carried out in the sub-routines (macros) called 'forward' and 'backward'. The sub-routines turn on the correct sequence of outputs to each coil in turn with a 0.1 second delay between each step. You can alter this time delay to make the stepper motor rotate faster or slower.

### Flowchart for controlling a stepper motor

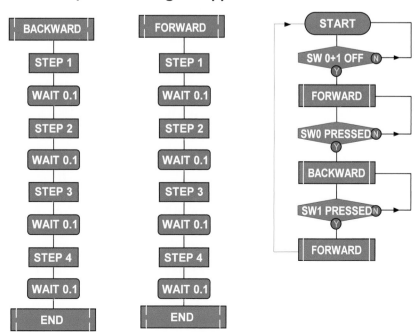

**Figure 3.111** *Stepper motor flowchart*

### Summary of PIC-Logicator flowchart

| Port Decision | SW 0+1 off | . . . . . . 0 0 |
| | SW0 PRESSED | . . . . . . . 1 |
| | SW1 PRESSED | . . . . . . 1 . |

| Port output functions forward | STEP 1 | 1 0 0 1 0 0 0 0 |
| | STEP 2 | 1 0 1 0 0 0 0 0 |
| | STEP 3 | 0 1 1 0 0 0 0 0 |
| | STEP 4 | 0 1 0 1 0 0 0 0 |

| Port output functions backward | STEP 1 | 0 1 1 0 0 0 0 0 |
| | STEP 2 | 1 0 1 0 0 0 0 0 |
| | STEP 3 | 1 0 0 1 0 0 0 0 |
| | STEP 4 | 0 1 0 1 0 0 0 0 |

| Macros | FORWARD |
| | BACKWARD |

This buggy was designed simply to move backwards and forwards. If you wished to make it turn you would need to use two stepper motors each one controlling a wheel. The PIC1684 is ideal for this as you have eight output lines. The simple buggy only used four of these (bits 4–7) you could use the remaining bits (0–3) for the second stepper motor. However, you will need to use two ULN2803A Darlington driver ICs as all the inputs and outputs were used for stepper motor 1 from the ULN2803A. This is simple matter of repeating the wiring used with the first ULN2803A with the inputs coming from bits 0–3 of the PIC16F84.

**Figure 3.112** *A two-motor buggy*

# PIC16F84 projects

| Example | **Arthritic aid** |

#### Design situation

A student's grandmother has arthritis in both hands and finds it difficult to unscrew the lids from jars. She was able to purchase a metal loop device to grip the lid but was unable to hold it in one hand. She was also unable to hold the jar securely. There was a need for a device that would hold jars of different sizes securely. This would allow the metal loop device to be used with both hands.

#### Solution

The final solution was a unit that sat on the table into which jars of different sizes could be placed. The jars were then held securely to allow the grandmother to use the metal loop with both hands. The final project is shown in Figure 3.113.

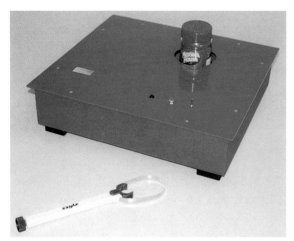

**Figure 3.113** *An arthritic aid for holding jars*

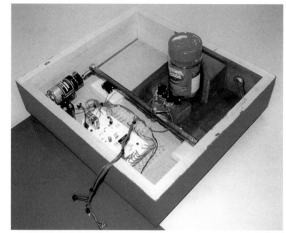

**Figure 3.114** *The circuit board and clamping unit*

### How it works

The jar is placed in the hole. A pressure sensor located at the bottom of the hole detects the jar and starts the PIC program. The PIC turns on a relay that controls a d.c. motor with a gearbox. The motor turns a threaded bar that moves the clamping arm to make contact with the jar. The arm has two micro-switches that act as sensors. When the two micro-switches are closed, the motor stops. When the grandmother has finished opening the jar, she presses a push-to-make switch located on the top of the unit. This reverses the motor releasing the grip on the jar. This is shown in Figure 3.114

A PIC16F84 was used and programmed using a PIC-Logicator. The face of the clamp was lined with the rubber from a toothed belt to increase the grip, while the long lever arm created a good mechanical advantage and increased the force at the clamping jaws.

| Example | **Metal combination lock safe** |
|---------|----------------------------------|

### *Design situation*

There has been an increase in the number of burglaries in the area. There is a need for a secure safe that can be bolted to the wall.

### *Solution*

The final solution was a metal box that used the PIC16F84 and a keypad to control a central locking unit. The final project is shown in Figures 3.115 and 6. The central locking unit was from the boot of an old Ford Escort and purchased for a few pounds from a local scrap yard.

**Figure 1.115** *Safe*

**Figure 1.116** *The inside of the safe*

### How it works

A metric keypad is used to open and close the safe. When the correct combination of numbers is entered in the correct sequence, the PIC switches on the relay that operates a central locking unit. The circuit board and keypad are shown in Figure 3.117. A key switch was added to the final project in the event that the PIC would fail.

**Figure 3.117** *Circuit board for the PIC16F84 combination lock*

| Example | Medication reminder |

### *Design situation*

An elderly gentleman living on his own, keeps forgetting to take his medication. The doctor was concerned and asked his grandson to help his grandfather. This was not a problem at the weekends but during school days there was no way the grandson could be there.

### Solution

The final solution was a medication reminder. The grandson placed the medication in three small containers before he left for school each day. At precise times during the day a buzzer would sound and an LED would flash to remind the grandfather to take his medication. The final solution is shown in Figure 3.118.

**Figure 3.118**

*Medication reminder project*

### How it works

The unit is controlled by a PIC16F84. Four inputs are used, one to start the program and the other three have to be pressed to cancel the buzzer and LED. The program was designed to turn on an output buzzer and LED every four hours. These outputs would stay on until the medication was taken and the input switch below that medication was pressed. The program would then move on to the next four-hour time period.

# PIC16F873

### PIC16F873 analogue and digital inputs

The PIC16F873 is a 28 pin IC. It has eight digital inputs, four

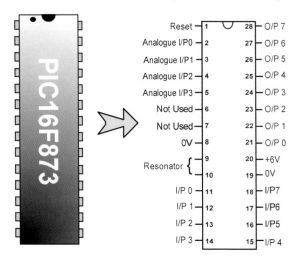

**Figure 3.119**

*PIC16F873 pin layout*

analogue inputs and eight outputs. You will need to connect it to a stable 6 V supply. Four 1.5 V AA batteries will be fine for this. This IC requires an external clock so you will need a 3-pin 4MHz ceramic resonator for this.

### Connecting the power supply

Pin 20 = + 6 V and pin 8/19 = 0 V. You will also need a 100 nF decoupling capacitor between pin 20 and 0 volts. This is shown in Figure 3.120.

### Connecting the digital inputs

Pins 11–18 are digital inputs 0–7. These can be either pulled high or low by means of 10–47 k resistors. In this example they are pulled low. When the switch is pressed, the PIC will detect a high. This is shown in Figure 3.121.

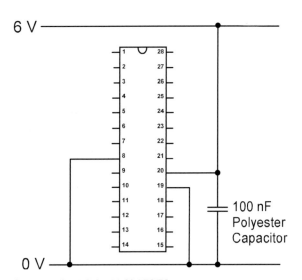

**Figure 3.120** *PIC16F873 connecting power*

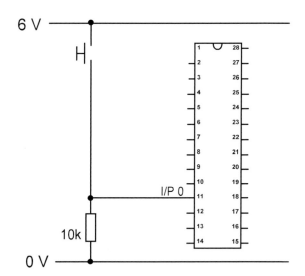

**Figure 3.121** *PIC16F873 Digital inputs*

### Connecting the analogue inputs

Pins 2–5 are analogue input pins. It is important to connect the sensor to the positive rail and the variable or fixed resistor to the negative rail. The analogue signal is taken from the middle point of this potential divider. The sensor should have a resistance of less than 10 k.

This is shown in Figure 3.122.

### Connecting the 3-pin resonator

Pins 9–10 should be connected to the two outside pins on the resonator. The middle leg is the negative and should be connected to the negative supply. You can connect the resonator either way round. This is shown in Figure 3.123.

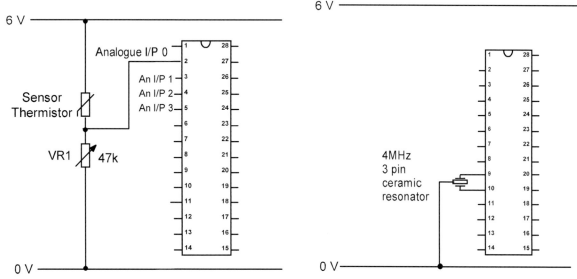

**Figure 3.122** *PIC16F873 analogue inputs*

**Figure 3.123** *PIC16F873 resonator*

### Connecting the outputs

Pins 21–28 are set as output. For all but LEDs, you will need to amplify the output signal coming from the PIC. This can be achieved simply by using the output signal to turn on a Darlington pair transistor. In the example shown in Figure 3.124, the buzzer is connected to the main power supply. When the transistor is on the buzzer will sound. The BCX38B is a good economical choice of Darlington pair transistor for most situations as its base collector current rating is 800 mA.

### Connecting the reset

Pin 1 is the reset. You must keep this high through a 10–47 k pull-up resistor. The push-to-make switch is connected between pin one and 0 volts. When this is pressed the PIC will reset. This is shown in Figure 3.125.

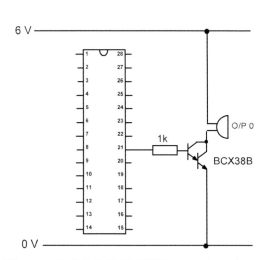

**Figure 3.124** *PIC16F873 amplifying the output signal*

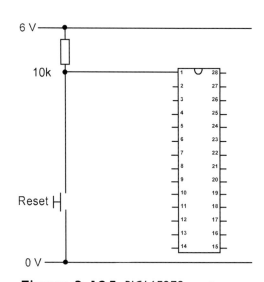

**Figure 3.125** *PIC16F873 reset*

### Circuit diagram for the PIC16F873

As explained, the PIC16F873 is a 28-pin IC. It has eight outputs, eight digital inputs and four analogue inputs. Designing a circuit incorporating the PIC16F873 is relatively straightforward in that you add power to the IC, connect the external clock in the form of a resonator and add a reset. Adding eight outputs is straightforward, you simply repeat the output circuit eight times. The same is true of the inputs. An example circuit is shown in Figure 3.126.

The four analogue input pins can each detect an analogue signal between 0 and 6 V. It is important to connect your sensor between the supply rail and one of the analogue pins. For best results the resistance of the sensor should not exceed 10 k. A suitable variable or fixed resistor should be connected between the analogue pin and the negative rail. The value of the variable or fixed resistor can be found during calibration. Calibration is explained later in the chapter.

A temperature-sensing circuit incorporating a thermistor, is shown in Figure 3.126. This produces an analogue signal to pin 1. The analogue signal is converted to a digital signal inside the PIC. The value of this digital signal will be between 0 and 255.

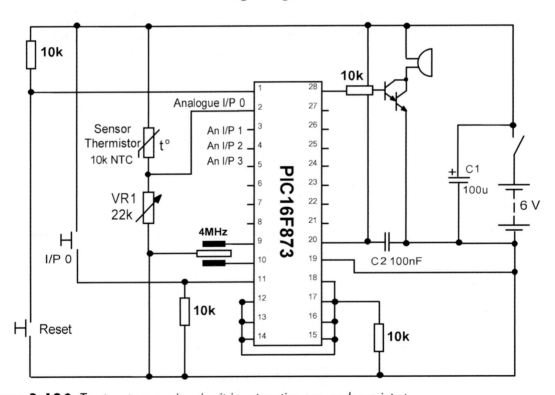

**Figure 3.126** *Temperature sensing circuit incorporating one analogue input.*

### PIC16F873 temperature sensing circuit

#### *Sensor circuit for the PIC16F873*

The circuit uses a 10 k bead thermistor with a 22 k variable resistor. The sensing temperature for this circuit was 10°C. The

10k resistor was selected because the resistance of the thermistor was found to be 4 k at 10°C. This kept the resistance below the desired 10 k. SW2 is a digital input used to start the project. The remaining seven inputs are pulled low to avoid false signals on the board.

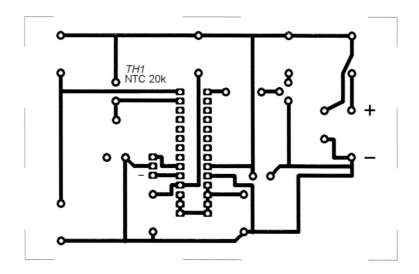

**Figure 3.127** *PCB for PIC16F873*

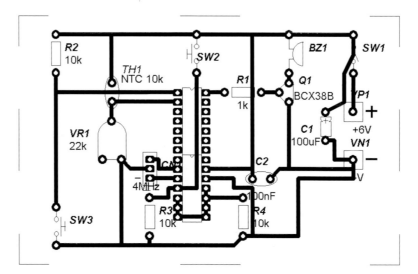

**Figure 3.128** *Silk screen for PIC16F873*

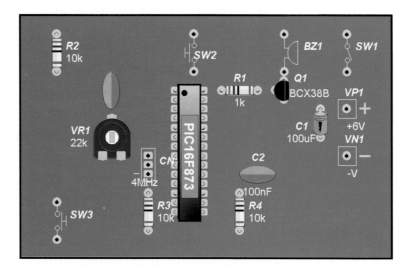

**Figure 3.129** *Top view of the PIC16F873 PCB*

### Bill of materials

NTC 10 k bead thermistor
1 × 100 µF Electrolytic capacitor
1 × 100 nF capacitor
1 × PIC16F873
1 × 28 pin DIL socket
1 × 4 MHz 3 pin ceramic resonator
3 × 10 k resistors
1 × 1 k resistor
1 × 22 k variable resistor
1 × BCX38B transistor
1 × 6 V buzzer
2 × push-to-make switch
1 × SPST toggle switch
1 × board 104.5 mm × 66.5 mm

### Sensing circuit using two analogue inputs

The PCBS shown in Figures 3.130–3 have two analogue sensors. The thermistor is connected to A0 while the LDR is connected to A1. The outputs are a buzzer and a bulb.

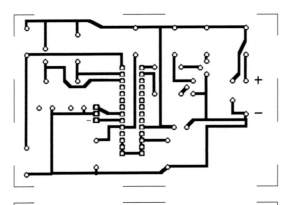

**Figure 3.130** *PCB for the two analogue input PIC16F873*

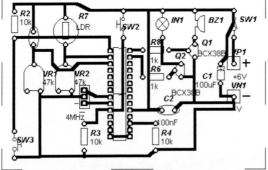

**Figure 3.131** *Silk screen for the two analogue input PIC16F873*

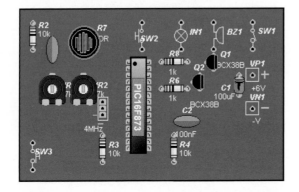

**Figure 3.132** *Top view of the two analogue input PIC16F873*

### Bill of materials

1 × NTC 10 k bead thermistor
1 × LDR
1 × 100 μF electrolytic capacitor
1 × 100 nF capacitor
1 × PIC16F873
1 × 28 pin DIL socket
1 × 4 MHz 3 pin ceramic resonator
3 × 10 k resistors
2 × 1 k resistor
2 × 47 k variable resistor
2 × BCX38B transistor
1 × 6 V buzzer
1 × 6V lamp
2 × push-to-make switch
1 × SPST toggle switch
1 × board 104.5 mm × 66.5 mm

Note: If you are unable to find a suitable 28 pin DIL socket, two 14 pin DIL sockets placed in series will do the same job.

# PIC analogue sensors

When designing PIC circuits that include an analogue sensor, it is good practice to add the sensor to the top half of the potential divider that produces the analogue signal. You should try to keep the resistance of the sensor at no more than 10 k as the current associated with the analogue voltage will be too low to be detected by the PIC. The selection of the variable resistor will depend on the sensor, but usually twice the sensing resistance works fine.

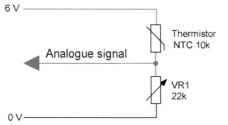

**Figure 3.133** *Analogue sensing circuit*

## Calibrating the analogue sensor

The analogue signal provided at the middle point of your potential divider must be converted to a series of digital signals which the PIC can recognise. The PIC will read a voltage between 0 and your supply voltage. Depending on the software you are using to program your PIC, the voltage will be converted to a series of digits. Most software packages use 0–255. Where zero voltage = 0 digits and maximum voltage = 255 digits.

Once you have decided on the sensor and variable resistor for your analogue signal, locate it in the environment where you plan to use it. This is to enable you to find out the voltage present at the analogue pin and to convert this to a number.

There are a number of methods you could use to do this. For the 0 – 255 scale you can buy a calibrating module that allows you to connect your sensor and variable resistor to it.

To use the module you would fix your sensor and variable resistor to it then locate it in the desired environment. The display would give you a reading, which you then use in your program. A commercial calibration module is shown in Figure 3.134.

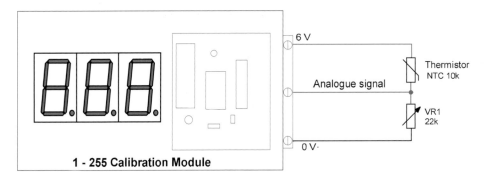

**Figure 3.134** *Commercial calibration module*

### Converting an analogue voltage into a numerical value for programming

It is possible to find the numerical value of an analogue signal so that you can use it in your program. To do this you will need to use a voltmeter and Ray's formula for PIC analogue-numerical values.

**Example 1**

1. Build the circuit. Remember the top resistor should be the sensor and be not more than 10 k. The bottom resistor should be at least the value of the resistance of the sensor.
2. Turn on the power supply.
3. Set your meter to voltage.
4. Place the meter's probes on the analogue pin and the negative rail of the PIC16F873.
5. Measure the voltage drop across these two points.
6. Measure the supply voltage.

The example shown in Figure 3.135 is a temperature-sensing circuit. The voltage drop (potential difference) between A0 and 0 volts was found to be 4.14 V. The room temperature was found to be 20° C. Therefore, 20° C = voltage drop between pin A0 and 0 volts which is 4.14 V. The supply voltage was found to be 6.20 V. It is important to work to two decimal places.

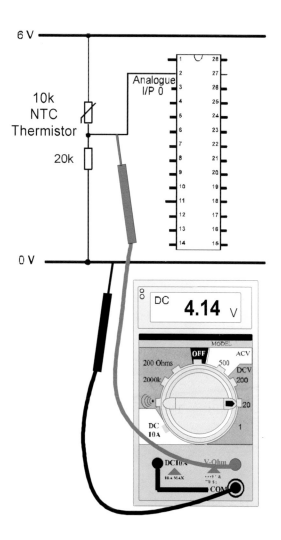

**Figure 3.135**

*Measuring the voltage*

You can now use these results to find the numerical value at pin 1 using 'Rays Formula'.

### Rays Formula for calculating analogue to digital (A–D) values

$$\text{Rays Formula} = \frac{\text{Voltage at analogue pin A0}}{\text{Supply voltage}} \times \frac{255}{1}$$

$$\text{Value} = \frac{4.14\text{V}}{6.20\text{V}} \times \frac{255}{1} = 172$$

Numerical value of A0 at $20°\,\text{C} = 172$

You can now use this value in your program.

### Using a numerical analogue value in your program

Having converted a temperature of $20°\,\text{C}$ to a numerical value of 172, you can now use this in your program. The value would be used with an IF–THEN statement in BASIC or if you are using PIC-Logicator, the value would be entered in a compare box.

### Using an analogue signal to control a cooling fan

The program in Figure 3.136 shows a short program used to

control a cooling fan. If you were using PIC-Logicator to program the PIC then you would use the compare cell in your flowchart. This cell monitors the value of the analogue signal coming in from the thermistor. If the analogue value is equal to or greater than 172, then the program would move along the yes route and turn on a cooling fan. If the value is less than 172, the program would move along the no route to keep the fan off. It is advisable to use the => symbols together as the value at A0 changes very quickly. If you use = only, then there is a possibility that the program might miss the precise value.

### PIC-Logicator flowchart for the temperature sensing circuit

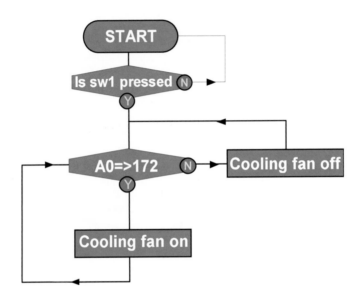

**Figure 3.136** *Flowchart for detecting an analogue signal*

### Summary of PIC-Logicator temperature sensing flowchart

Start
Port decision            Is SW1 pressed        . . . . . . . 1
Port compare             Analogue channel A0=> 172

Port output functions    Buzzer off            0 0 0 0 0 0 0 0
                         Buzzer on             0 0 0 0 0 0 0 1

# PIC16F627

The PIC16F627 is an 18 pin IC. It is a new PIC designed to replace the PIC16F84. It has five digital inputs, two analogue inputs and 8 outputs. It will need a stable 5–6 V d.c. power supply. Four 1.5 V AA batteries will be fine for this. The IC has an internal clock that does away with the need for a 4 MHz resonator making circuit design that much easier. As with the PIC16F84 you will need to add a reset push-to-make switch to enable you to reset the program.

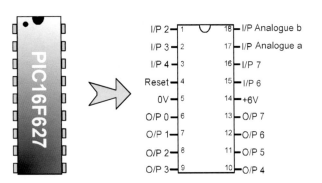

**Figure 3.137** *PIC 16F627 pin layout*

### Connecting the power supply

Pin 14 = + 6 V and pin 5 = 0 V. You will also need a 100 nF decoupling capacitor between pin 14 and 0 V and a 100 μF smoothing capacitor across the supply.

### Connecting the reset

Pin 4 = reset. You must keep this high to enable the PIC to work, but once the reset switch is pressed, the program will reset.

### Connecting the digital inputs

Pins 1–3 and 15 and 16 are the inputs. You would normally tie the inputs low through a 10 k resistor then, by using switch, offer a high to the pin.

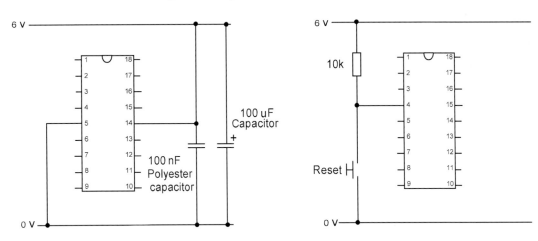

**Figure 3.138** *Power*

**Figure 3.139** *Reset*

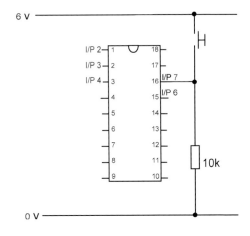

**Figure 3.140** *Digital inputs*

## Connecting the analogue inputs

The PIC16F627 has two analogue inputs. These inputs will detect an analogue signal. Unfortunately, it is only capable of detecting ⅔ the supply voltage and converting this to a numerical value between 0 and 160 instead of the normal 0–255 range.

You will need to build a potential divider circuit to act as input sensor. The top resistor should be ⅓ the total value and the bottom two resistors making up the remaining ⅔. In figure 3.141 shows a suitable analogue circuit with a multimeter used to find the voltage present at pin 17. By using Ray's formula it is possible to find the numerical value of this voltage. This numerical value would then be used in your program.

A voltage greater than ⅔ the supply will not damage the PIC but it will continue to read this as a value 160. Another problem with this PIC is that it functions on 16 steps called 'low resolution readings'. Low-resolution readings will detect your voltage and convert this to the **nearest** step in the 16 sequences.

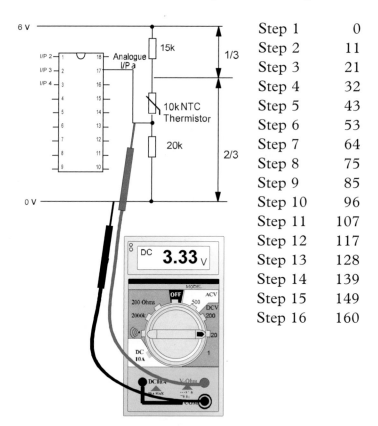

| | |
|---|---|
| Step 1 | 0 |
| Step 2 | 11 |
| Step 3 | 21 |
| Step 4 | 32 |
| Step 5 | 43 |
| Step 6 | 53 |
| Step 7 | 64 |
| Step 8 | 75 |
| Step 9 | 85 |
| Step 10 | 96 |
| Step 11 | 107 |
| Step 12 | 117 |
| Step 13 | 128 |
| Step 14 | 139 |
| Step 15 | 149 |
| Step 16 | 160 |

**Figure 3.141** *Analogue input circuit for the PIC 16F627*

# CHAPTER FOUR  **Higher Pneumatics**

## Sequential control

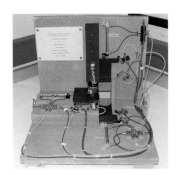

**Figure 4.1** *Pneumatic aluminium can crusher*

When two or more cylinders are required to operate one after the other, then a way to do this is through an arrangement called sequential control. An example of an aluminium can crusher project using sequential control is shown in Figure 4.1.

To understand sequential control it is important first to come to terms with the language.

The first thing you need to do is to give each cylinder in the sequence a letter. In Figure 4.2–3 the two cylinders are labelled A and B.

The next thing you must do is to state the position of the cylinders in terms of negative or positive (− +). A cylinder in the negative position (−) is shown in Figure 4.4.

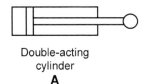

Double-acting cylinder
**A**

**Figure 4.2** *Labelling cylinder A*

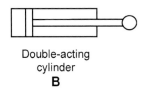

Double-acting cylinder
**B**

**Figure 4.3** *Labelling cylinder B*

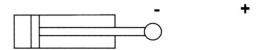

**Figure 4.4** *Cylinder in the negative position*

It is now possible to describe cylinders A/B in terms of positive or negative. Cylinder A − and cylinder B − or simply, A − B −.

The next stage in designing the circuit is to ensure that each cylinder is controlled by a pilot/pilot air operated 5/2 valve. Finally 3/2 valves are used to provide the air signals that are used to change the state of the pilot/pilot air operated 5/2 vales in the correct sequence.

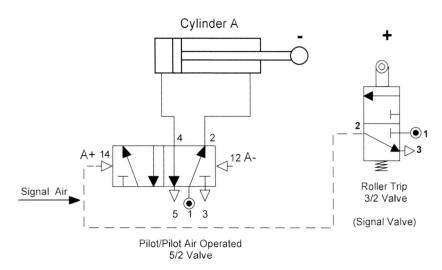

**Figure 4.5** *Sending a signal to the pilot/pilot air operated 5/2 valve*

## Sequential control – second stage

The next stage in designing a circuit that contains sequential control is to add cylinder B along with the remaining 5/2 control valve and the 3/2 signal valves. The circuit diagram shown in Figure 4.6 indicates the position of the cylinders and valves for the sequence: start, A +, B +, A −, B −.

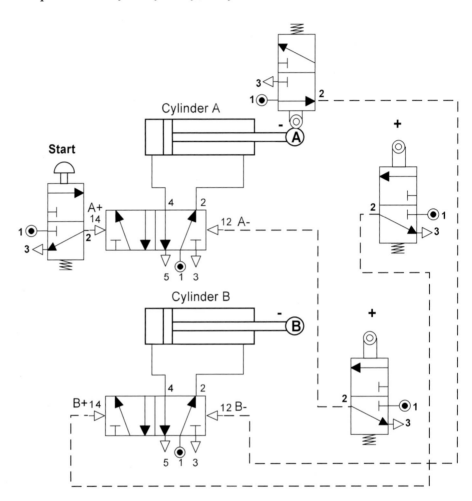

**Figure 4.6** *Circuit diagram for the sequence: start, A +, B+, A −, B −*

There are a limited number of permutations you can have in sequential control using roller trip and plunger-operated 3/2 valves. These are called operative systems and include:

Start, A +, B+, A −, B −.
Start, A+, B −, A −, B+.
Start, A −, B −, A+, B+.
Start, B+, A+, B −, A −.
Start, B −, A −, B+, A+.
Start, B+, A −, B −, A+.

It is also possible to have any of these permutations running continuously.

### The sequence: start, A+, B +, A −, B −, explained

**Sequence A+.** Actuate the start valve IS1 by pressing the push-button 3/2 valve. This will change the 5/2 valve to a 14 state. This will make cylinder A go positive. This is shown in Figure 4.7.

**Sequence B +.** Piston rod A actuates roller trip IS2. This sends an air signal to the lower 5/2 valve that changes its state to 14. When this happens, cylinder B goes positive. This is shown in Figure 4.8.

**Sequence A−.** Piston rod B actuates roller trip IS3. This sends an air signal to the top 5/2 valve that changes its state to 12. When this happens, cylinder A goes negative. This is shown in Figure 4.9.

**Sequence B−.** Piston rod A actuates roller trip IS4. This sends an air signal to the lower 5/2 valve that changes its state to 12. When this happens, cylinder B goes negative. This is shown in Figure 4.10.

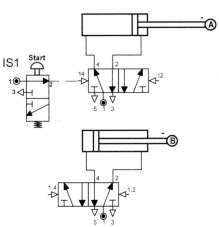

**Figure 4.7** *Achieving the sequence A +*

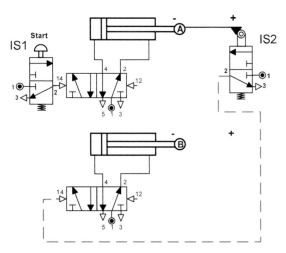

**Figure 4.8** *Achieving the sequence B+*

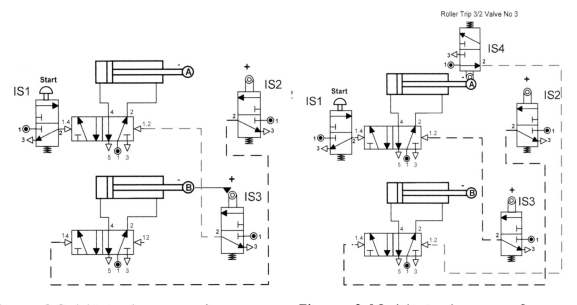

**Figure 4.9** *Achieving the sequence A−*

**Figure 4.10** *Achieving the sequence B−*

## Building the sequence: start, A+, B+, A −, B −

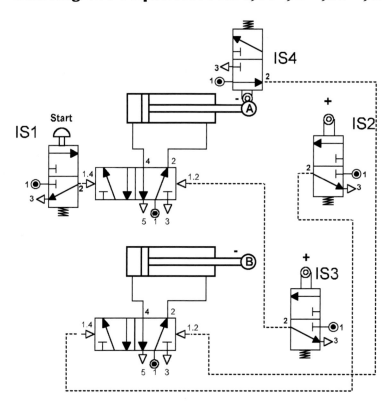

**Figure 4.11** *Complete circuit diagram for the sequence start, A+, B +, A −, B −*

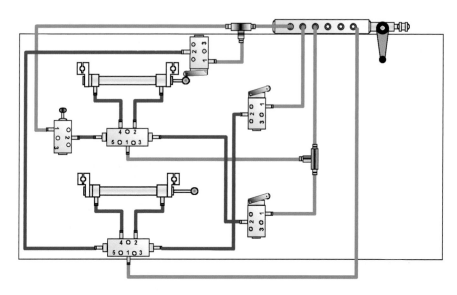

**Figure 4.12** *Modelling the circuit for the sequence start, A+, B +, A −, B −*

| Example | Incorporating the sequence: A+, B +, A −, B −, into a product |
|---------|---------------------------------------------------------------|

### Design situation

Design a working model of a pneumatic system that would feed snack bars into a wrapping machine. The system must push snack bars out of the hopper using push rod 1, then down a chute, which is at 90° to the hopper, into a wrapping machine using push rod 2. Cams 1 and 2 can be used in conjunction with roller trip 3/2 valves as a means of obtaining the correct air signals.

### Solution

The solution incorporated sequential control A +, B +, A −, B −, to push the snack bars down the chute and then push them through 90° into the wrapping machine. The drawings in Figure 4.13 were used to design the model and the picture in Figure 4.14 shows the final product.

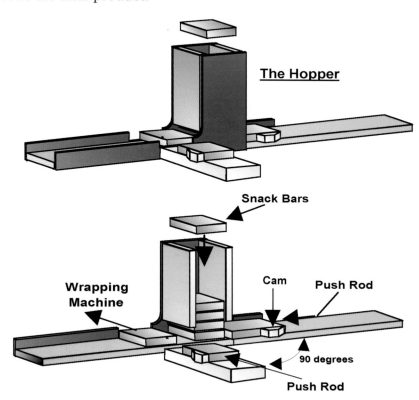

**Figure 4.13** *Concept sketches of the hopper*

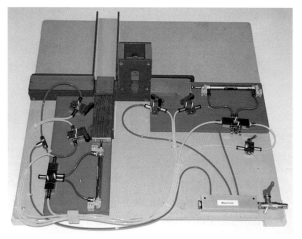

**Figure 4.14** *The final product piped in the sequence A +, B +, A −, B−*

## Circular diagrams

The operating sequence for sequential control circuits can be expressed in a number of different ways. One of the most common is the circular diagram.

An example of a circular diagram for the sequence, A +, B +, A −, B−, is shown in figure 4.15.

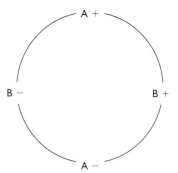

**Figure 4.15** *Circular diagram for A +, B +, A−, B−*

The circuit diagram for this continuous sequence is shown in Figure 4.16

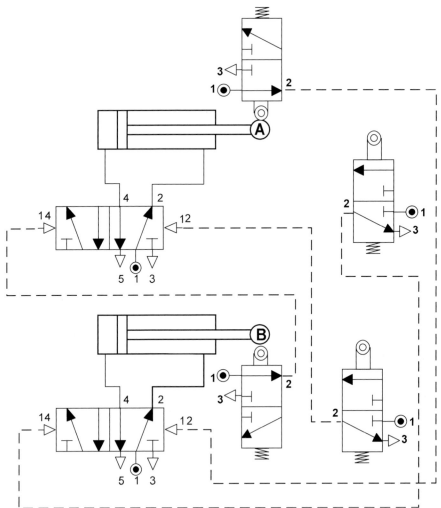

**Figure 4.16** *Circuit diagram for continuous, A +, B +, A−, B−*

## Adding a stop/start to the sequence, A +, B +, A -, B -

The previous circuit ran continuously once it was connected to the main air supply.

It is important to add a start/stop switch to the sequence. This is usually a lever operated 3/2 valve and its location in the circuit is crucial if the sequence is to start and stop in correct location. The circular diagram for this sequence is shown in figure 4.17. The positioning of the start/stop would be after B – and before A +.

## Circuit design for the sequence: start, A+, B−, A−, B+

This circuit starts when the push-button operated 3/2 valve is pressed and released. The circuit is designed to complete one sequence then wait until the start button is pressed again.

The circular diagram for this sequence is shown in figure 4.19. The positioning of the start would be before A+.

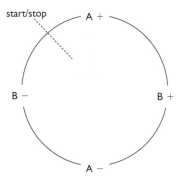

**Figure 4.17** *Circular diagram A +, B +, A−, B−*

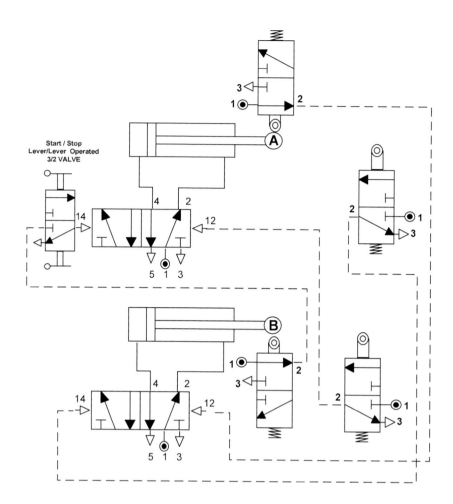

**Figure 4.18** *Circuit diagram for the sequence: stop/start, A +, B +, A −, B−*

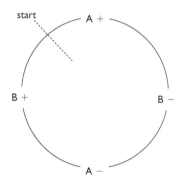

**Figure 4.19** *Circular diagram for start, A+, B−, A−, B+*

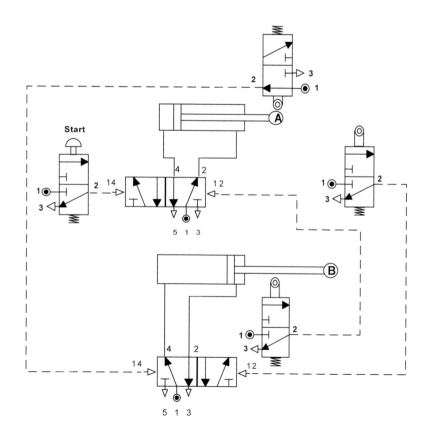

**Figure 4.20** *Circuit diagram for the sequence: start, A+, B−, A−, B+*

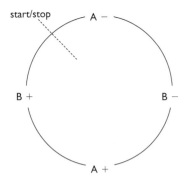

**Figure 4.21** *Circular diagram for: start/stop, A−, B −, A +, B +*

## Circuit design for the sequence: start/stop, A−, B −, A +, B +

This circuit starts and stops when both cylinders A and B are negative. As the circuit has to run continuously until it is switched off a lever/lever operated 3/2 valve is used as the start/stop switch. When a valve is on, then it should be shown in the actuated position. In this circuit the piston rod of both cylinder A and B are causing the right-hand 3/2 valves to be actuated. The circular diagram for this sequence is shown in Figure 4.21.

The positioning of the start/stop should be after B+ and before A −.

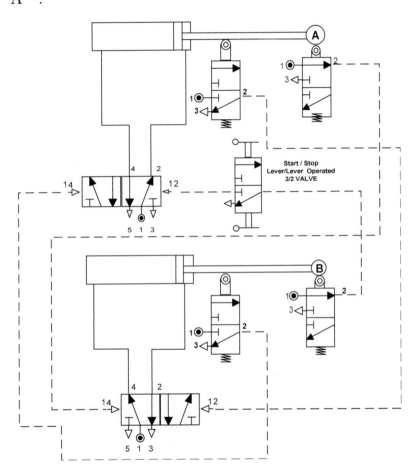

**Figure 4.22** *Circuit design for the sequence: start/stop, A−, B −, A +, B +*

## Three double-acting cylinders in sequence: start/stop, A +, B +, C +, A −, B− C−

The circular diagram for this sequence is shown in Figure 4.23.

The positioning of the start/stop comes after C − and before A +.

The circuit design for the sequence: start/stop, A+, B+, C+, A−, B− C− is shown in Figure 4.24.

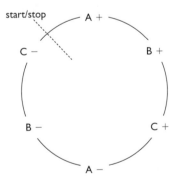

**Figure 4.23** *Circular diagram for: atart/stop, A +, B +, C +, A −, B− C−*

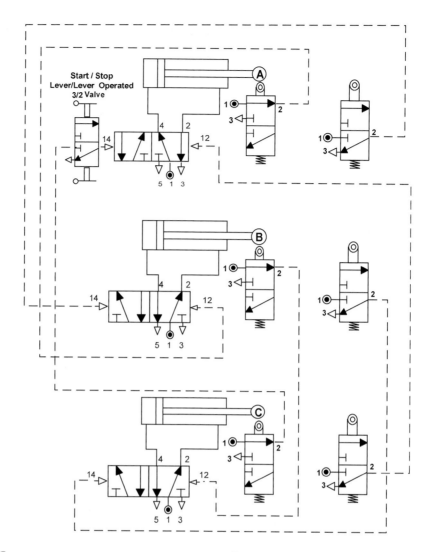

**Figure 4.24** *Circuit design for the sequence: start/stop, A +, B +, C +, A −, B− C−*

# Calculating force, pressure and area

The formula for calculating force, pressure or area is:
**Force = Pressure × Area**.

- Force is measured in Newtons (N)
- Pressure is measured in $N/mm^2$ (1 Bar = 0.1 $N/mm^2$)
- Area is measured in $mm^2$ (area of a circle = $\pi r^2$)

Note: Pressure should be expressed in $N/m^2$ but due to the small-diameter cylinders you will be working with in technology, it is common to give pressure as $N/mm^2$.

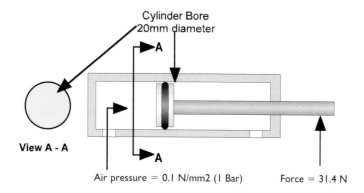

Cylinder Bore 20mm diameter

View A - A

Air pressure = 0.1 N/mm2 (1 Bar)    Force = 31.4 N

**Figure 4.25** *Calculating force*

To calculate the force asserted by this piston you would use the formula: $F = P \times A$.

$F$ = pressure $\times$ area
$F = 0.1\text{N/mm}^2 \times \pi r^2$
$F = 0.1 \times (3.14 \times 10 \times 10)$
$F = 0.1 \times 314$
$F = 31.4\,\text{N}$

The force asserted by the piston $= 31.4\,\text{N}$
Air pressure $= 0.1\,\text{N/mm}^2$ (1Bar) Force $= 31.4\,\text{N}$

The force asserted by the piston as it goes positive is always greater than that asserted as it goes negative. This is due to the fact that the surface area of the piston is greater at the back of the piston than at the front. The area of the **piston rod** must be subtracted to give the surface area on the front side.

A cut-away view of a double-acting cylinder is shown in Figure 4.26. The surface area is greater at the back of the piston than at the front.

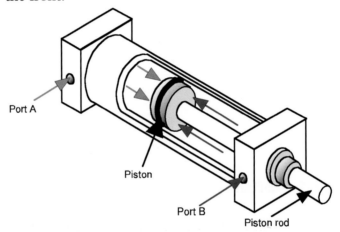

**Figure 4.26** *Cut-away view of a double-acting cylinder*

## Calculating the force as the piston goes positive and negative

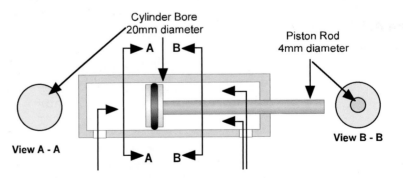

**Figure 4.27** *Positive and negative force*

View A – A shows how the surface area at the back of the piston is greater than at the front.

Area A – A $= \pi R^2$
$\qquad\qquad = 3.14 \times (\text{radius} \times \text{radius})$
$\qquad\qquad = 3.14 \times (10 \times 10)$
$\qquad\qquad = 314\,\text{mm}^2$

View B – B shows how the surface area at the front is less by the area of the piston rod.

Area B – B = (area of the piston− area of the piston rod)
= $(\pi R^2) - (\pi r^2)$
= $3.14 \times (R \times R) - 3.14 \times (r \times r)$
= $3.14 \times (10 \times 10) - 3.14 \times (2 \times 2)$
= $314 - 12.56$
= $301.44 \, \text{mm}^2$

Now that you know the area of the piston on both sides, you can calculate the positive going force and the negative going force.

### Calculating the force as the piston goes positive

Force = $P \times A$
Force = $0.1 \times 314$
Force = $31.4 \, \text{N}$

### Calculating the force as the piston goes negative

Force = $P \times A$
Force = $0.1 \times 301.44$
Force = $30.144 \, \text{N}$

**View A - A**

**View B - B**

**Figure 4.28** *View of the surface area of the piston for the positive and negative strokes*

# Electro-pneumatics

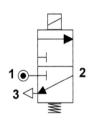

**Figure 4.29** *Symbol for a solenoid valve*

Electro-pneumatics is an electronic method of controlling 3/2 and 5/2 solenoid valves. The actuation (turning on) of the valve is achieved by applying an electrical signal to the solenoid. The solenoid is fixed to the top of the valve. When the signal is present the solenoid pushes the spool down to change the flow through the valve from 2–3 to 1–2. This is shown in Figures 4.31 and 4.32.

### How it works

The solenoid is an electromotive device that has a soft metal core surrounded by a copper coil. When there is no electrical signal present at the coil the spring at the base of the valve keeps the soft metal core in the up position. In this state the valve is off. This is shown in Figure 4.31.

When a signal is present, the coil becomes a magnet pushing the soft metal core downwards. This is shown in Figure 4.32. Remove the signal and the valve goes back to the unactuated (off) state.

**Figure 4.30** *A solenoid operated 3/2 valve*

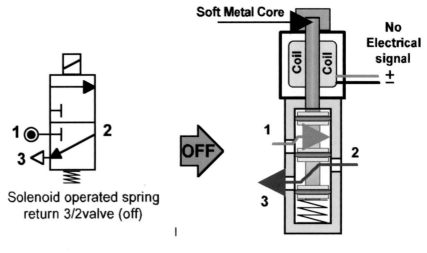

**Figure 4.31** *Solenoid operated 3/2 valve in the off position*

Solenoid operated spring return 3/2valve (off)

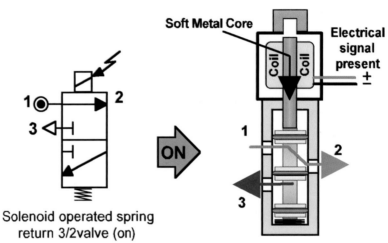

**Figure 4.32** *Solenoid operated 3/2 valve in the on position*

Solenoid operated spring return 3/2valve (on)

## Electro-pneumatics: types of valves

Both 3/2 and 5/2 pneumatic valves can be actuated by a solenoid. It is possible to have valves solenoid operated/spring return or solenoid/solenoid operated. These are shown in Figure 4.33 and Figure 4.34.

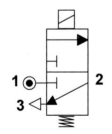

**Figure 4.33** *Symbol for a solenoid operated /spring return 3/2 valve*

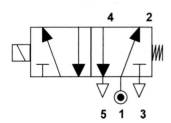

**Figure 4.34** *Symbol for a solenoid operated /spring return 5/2 valve*

**Figure 4.35** *A solenoid operated/spring return 5/2 valve*

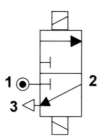

**Figure 4.36** *Symbol for solenoid/solenoid operated 3/2 valve*

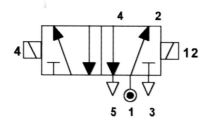

**Figure 4.37** *Symbol for a solenoid/solenoid operated 5/2 valve*

**Figure 4.38** *A solenoid/solenoid operated 5/2 valve*

# Switching solenoid valves

Any one of a number of electronic switches can be used to actuate a solenoid valve.

The most commonly used switches are normally open micro-switches, push-to-make switches, reed switches, relays and toggle switches. A micro-switch connected to a battery and solenoid operated/spring return 3/2 valve is shown in Figure 4.39. When the switch is closed, the current will flow to the solenoid making it come on.

A ladder diagram representing the simple electro-pneumatic circuit incorporating a solenoid operated/spring return 3/2 valve is shown in Figure 3.40.

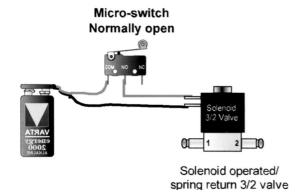

**Figure 4.39** *Basic electro-pneumatic solenoid operated/spring return 3/2 valve*

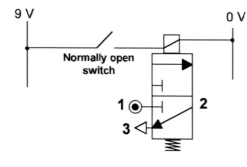

**Figure 4.40** *Ladder diagram for the circuit shown in Figure 4.39*

## Electro-pneumatic symbols

The following are some of the most commonly used symbols for electronic components. These are shown in Figure 4.41. You will need to know these symbols when building the circuits in this book.

### Electrical switches

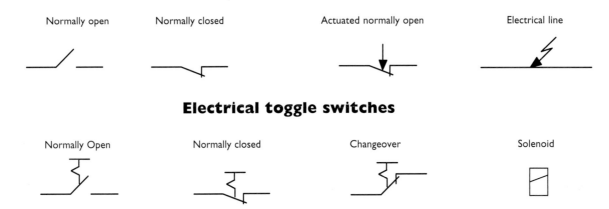

### Electrical toggle switches

**Figure 4.41** *Switch symbols*

## Designing electro-pneumatic circuits using ladder diagrams

Electro-pneumatic circuits can be drawn as ladder diagrams. These diagrams have a vertical positive and a parallel negative rail. The circuit is then drawn horizontally in between.

**Example**

A student was asked to design a circuit that would cause a single-acting cylinder to go positive when a normally open switch is closed. The 3/2 valve should be actuated by means of a solenoid. The student designed the circuit using a normally open switch that was connected between the positive rail and the solenoid on the 3/2 valve. The other side of the solenoid was then joined to the 0 volts rail. This is shown in Figure 4.42.

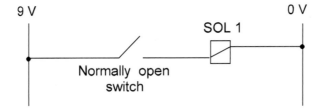

**Figure 4.42** *Ladder showing the solenoid off*

When the switch was closed, the solenoid was actuated. The symbol for an electrical line, i.e. current flowing down the line, is now added to the diagram. This is shown in Figure 4.43.

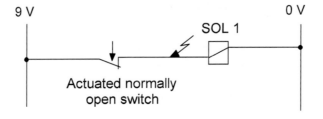

**Figure 4.43** *Ladder showing the solenoid on*

## AND logic function using electro-pneumatics

Electrical switches can be arranged in series to form an AND logic circuit. The circuit diagram shown in Figure 4.44 is designed to control a solenoid operated/spring return 3/2 valve AND logic. This system could be used in safety situations such as safety guards on cutting machine.

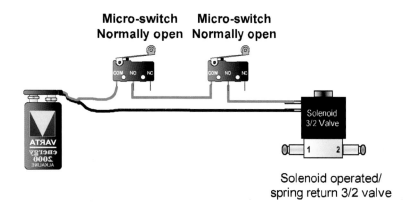

**Figure 4.44** *Drawing of the AND logic circuit*

Solenoid operated/
spring return 3/2 valve

## How it works

When switch 1 and switch 2 are closed then the solenoid will change to on. Main air can then pass through the 3/2 valve to make the single-acting cylinder go positive. If one or more of the switches is opened then the 3/2 valve will change to off and the single-acting cylinder will go negative.

## Ladder Diagram for AND logic

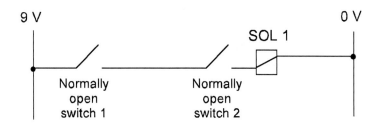

**Figure 4.45** *Ladder diagram incorporating two normally open switches in AND logic*

## Symbol diagrams

The AND logic circuit shown in Figure 4.44 can also be drawn using symbols. The symbol version, called a symbolic diagram, is shown in Figure 4.46.

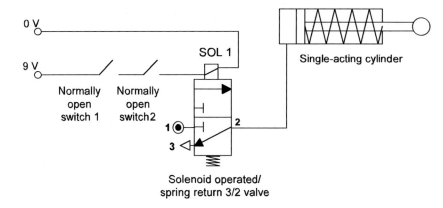

**Figure 4.46** *Symbolic diagram of an electro-pneumatic AND logic circuit*

## OR logic function using electro-pneumatics

Electrical switches can be arranged in parallel to form an OR logic circuit. The circuit is designed to control solenoid 1 (SOL 1) on a solenoid operated/spring return 3/2 valve. In this circuit, if you close either normally opened switch 1 or normally opened switch 2, then 9 volts will go to SOL 1. The circuit for this is shown in Figure 4.46.

## Ladder Diagram

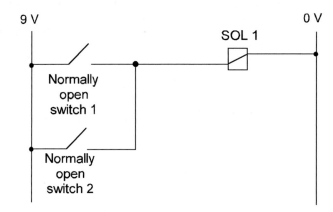

**Figure 4.46** *Ladder diagram of two normally open switches in 'OR' logic*

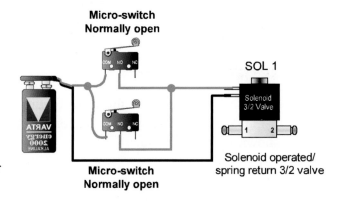

**Figure 4.47** *Drawing of an OR logic circuit*

## Symbol diagrams

This circuit can also be drawn using a symbol diagram. The symbol version is shown in figure 4.48.

194

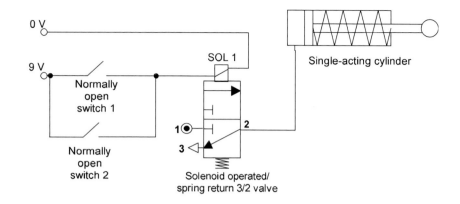

**Figure 4.48** *Symbol diagram of two normally open switches in OR logic*

## How it works

When switch 1 or switch 2 are closed, then the solenoid will change to on. Main air can then pass through the 3/2 valve to make the single-acting cylinder go positive. When both switches are opened, then the 3/2 valve will change to off and the single-acting cylinder will go negative. This system could be used to operate a pneumatic shop door where the door is required to be opened from the inside or the outside.

## Electro-pneumatic switching using a toggle switch

If you wish to use a solenoid/solenoid operated 3/2 or 5/2 valve in your circuit, then only one solenoid can be on at any one time. This can be achieved in a number of different ways, such as using a changeover switch. An example of this is shown Figure 4.49. The circuit incorporates a toggle changeover switch to control solenoid 1 or 2.

## Ladder Diagram

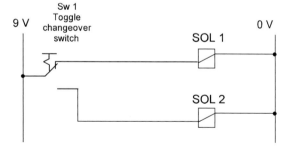

**Figure 4.49** *Ladder diagram for a solenoid/ solenoid operated 5/2 valve*

## How it works

When SW1 is in the up position, solenoid 1 will be on. This will cause the 5/2 valve to change over to a 12 combination. In this state the double-acting cylinder will go negative. When SW1 is in the down position then the 5/2 valve will change over to a 14 combination. In this state the double-acting cylinder will go positive.

## Symbol diagram incorporating a solenoid/solenoid operated 5/2 valve

The circuit shown in Figure 4.49 can also be drawn using symbols. The symbol version is shown in Figure 4.50.

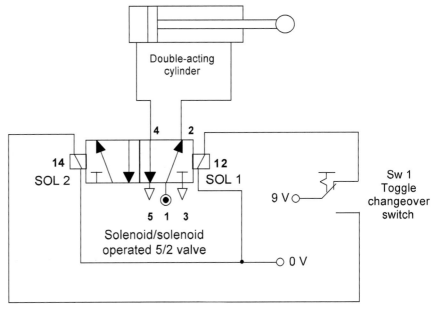

**Figure 4.50** *Symbol diagram incorporating a solenoid/solenoid operated 5/2 valve*

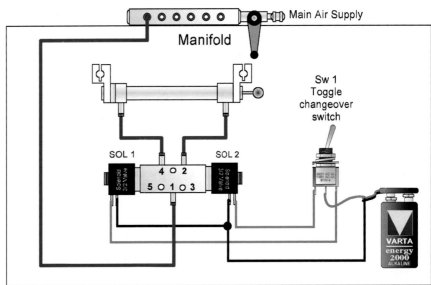

**Figure 4.51** *Drawing of a circuit containing a solenoid/solenoid operated 5/2 valve*

## Electro-pneumatic switching using 2 SPST switches

It is possible to control a solenoid/solenoid operated 5/2 valve using two SPST switches. An example of this is shown in the ladder diagram in Figure 4.52.

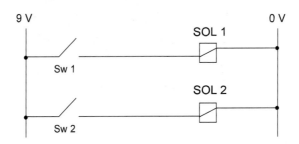

**Figure 4.52** *Ladder diagram incorporating two SPST switches*

## Symbol diagram incorporating two SPST switches

The ladder diagram in Figure 4.52 can also be drawn using symbols. The symbol version is shown in Figure 4.53.

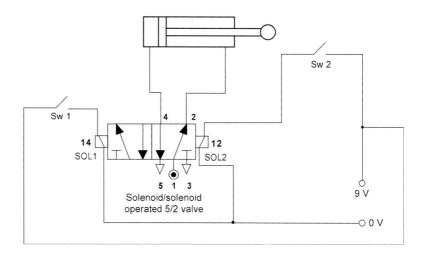

**Figure 4.53** *Symbol diagram incorporating two SPST switches*

## How it works

When switch 1 is closed momentarily, solenoid 1 will be actuated. When this happens the solenoid/solenoid operated 5/2 valve will change over allowing a flow of air in port 1 and out of port 4 (a 14 combination). This will cause the double-acting cylinder to go positive. When the piston rod hits switch 2, solenoid 2 will cause the solenoid/solenoid operated 5/2 valve to change over allowing a flow of air in port 1 and out of port 2 (a 12 combination) making the double-acting cylinder go negative. If the switches are arranged as shown in Figure 4.54, then you will have reciprocating motion.

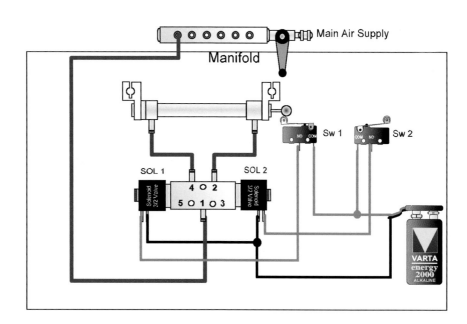

**Figure 4.54** *Drawing of a reciprocating motion electro-pneumatic circuit*

## Ladder diagram for sequential control of two cylinders

*Electro-pneumatic sequence: start/stop, A +, B +, A −, B−*

When designing electro-pneumatic circuits using ladder diagrams it is important to explain that each solenoid is controlled by one or more limit switches.

For example, switches 6 and 5 control the sequence A+. This is shown in Figure 4.55.

The solenoids and limit switches for the above sequence would be:

- Solenoid 1 on: cylinder A goes positive
- Solenoid 2 on: cylinder B goes positive
- Solenoid 3 on: cylinder A goes negative
- Solenoid 4 on: cylinder B goes negative

From this you can work out the switching arrangement for each solenoid.

- Switch 1 provides an on/off for the power supply.
- When switches 6 and 5 are closed, this actuates solenoid 1, making cylinder A go positive.
- When switch 3 is closed, this actuates solenoid 2, making cylinder B go positive.
- When switch 4 is closed, this actuates solenoid 3, making cylinder A go negative.
- When switch 2 is closed, this actuates solenoid 4, making cylinder B go negative.
- Switch 6 is the stop/start for the sequence.

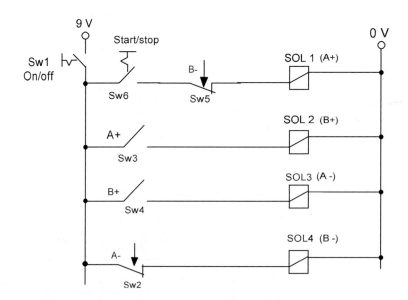

**Figure 4.55** *Ladder diagram for the sequence: start/stop, A +, B +, A −, B −*

*Electro-pneumatic circuit diagram for the sequence: start/stop, A +, B +, A −, B−*

**Sequence A +**. When cylinder B is negative and the manual switch 6 is closed an electrical signal is present at solenoid 1 on the 5/2 valve that gives you a 14 combination. This causes cylinder A to go positive.

**Sequence B +.** Piston rod A closes switch 3. This sends an electrical signal to solenoid 2 on the 5/2 valve that changes its combination to 14. When this happens, cylinder B goes positive.

**Sequence A.** Piston rod B closes switch 4. This sends an electrical signal to solenoid 3 on the 5/2 valve that changes its combination to 12. When this happens, cylinder A goes negative.

**Sequence B.** Piston rod A closes switch 2. This sends an electrical signal to solenoid 4 on the 5/2 valve that changes its combination back to 12. When this happens, cylinder B goes negative.

This sequence will repeat until the stop/start switch is opened again or the power is switched off. This is shown in Figure 4.56.

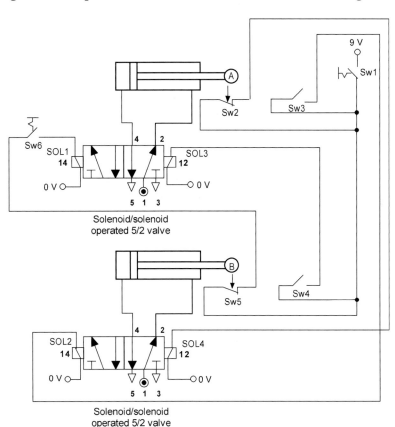

**Figure 4.56** *Circuit diagram for the sequence: start/stop, A +, B +, A −, B−*

## Cylinder mountings

When incorporating cylinders into your project, it is important to connect them correctly. The cylinder should be held firmly to enable continuous operation without movement. The same mounting can be used with both single-acting and double-acting cylinders.

### Static cylinders

When a cylinder is fixed rigid in a static position then angle brackets can be used.

### Foot mountings

Angle brackets are fixed front and rear to give a secure foot fixing.

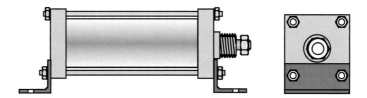

**Figure 4.57** *Angle brackets*

### Section through foot mountings

Section through the angle bracket showing the use of the cylinder bolts as a means of fixing the cylinder.

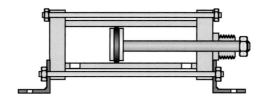

**Figure 4.58** *Bolting the angle brackets to the cylinder*

### Single foot mounting

Single foot mounting fixed to the bearing housing.

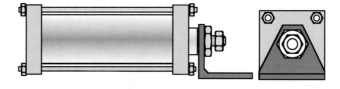

**Figure 4.59** *Single foot mounting*

Single foot mountings and /or angle brackets can be used to hold a cylinder securely when pushing an object off a conveyor belt. This is shown in Figure 4.60

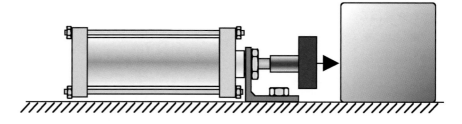

**Figure 4.60** *Single foot mounting*

## Mounting pivoting cylinder

In situations where cylinders are required to pivot as they go positive and negative then you must use fixing which allows for this pivoting movement. An example of this is shown in Figure 4.61. When the piston pulls the lever into position 1, the cylinder moves on the back pivot. The front pivot allows for movement at the lever. When the piston pushes the lever to position 2 the cylinder must be free to pivot up again.

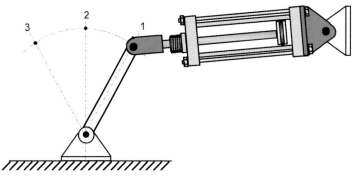

**Figure 4.61** *Cylinder in the negative position*

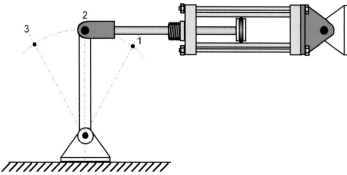

**Figure 4.62** *Cylinder in the positive position*

## Pivot mountings

### Clevis

A clevis mounting should be used when the cylinder must pivot. The clevis is designed to screw on to the threaded end of the piston rod or you can use a rear clevis if both ends of the cylinder are to pivot. An axle passes through the forked end of the clevis and through the object being pushed and pulled.

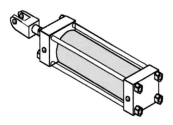

**Figure 4.63** *Front clevis*

### Other pivot mountings

The type of mounting used will depend on the situation and operation of the cylinder. The combination of front and end mounting and fixings can be different from the ones shown but they are all designed to allow the cylinder to pivot about a point.

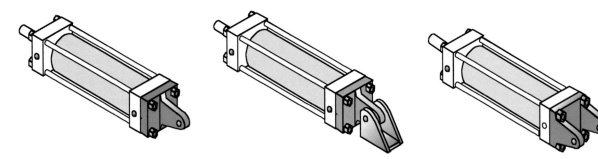

**Figure 4.64** *Rear eye mounting*    **Figure 4.65** *Rear hinge mounting*    **Figure 4.66** *Rear clevis mounting*

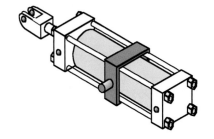

**Figure 4.67** *Trunnion mounting*

**201**

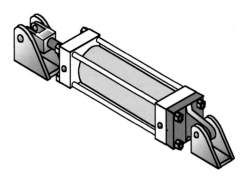

**Figure 4.68** *Pivot fixings at both ends of the cylinder*

The arrangement for fixing a cylinder that has to pivot at both ends is shown in Figure 4.68.

Hinged mountings are used at both ends of the cylinder. A front clevis is screwed to the piston rod. An eye mounting is used at the rear.

| Example | Electro-pneumatic car park barrier |
|---|---|

### Design situation

A local garage wanted a pneumatically operated barrier to prevent unlawful parking at the rear of the premises. The barrier had to have a system that allowed the staff to park but no one else.

### Solution

The solution was an electro-pneumatic barrier operated by means of a shaped key. A sensor in the road closed the barrier after the car had entered the car premises. The system worked as follows:

- The barrier opened when a specially shaped key was inserted into a slot.
- The key was designed to activate two micro-switches in **AND** logic.
- When the correct key was used, the barrier would open and allow the car to pass into the car park.
- Closing of the barrier was by means of a sensor in the road. This sensor had two micro-switches in **OR** logic. Pressing any one of these switches would cause the barrier to come down.
- The means of raising and lowering the barrier was a double-acting cylinder controlled by a **solenoid/solenoid operated 5/2 valve**.

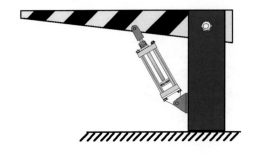

**Figure 4.69** *Barrier in the down position*

- The double-acting cylinder was required to pivot so a **front clevis mounting** was used at the piston rod end and a **rear eye mounting and rear hinge mounting** at the bottom.

**Figure 4.70** *Barrier in the raised position*

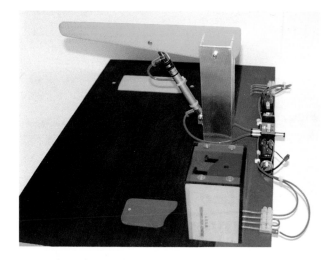

**Figure 4.71** *Picture of the barrier*

### Ladder diagram for the barrier

Solenoid 1 is actuated by micro-switch 1 or micro-switch 2. The micro-switches are arranged in OR logic. When one or both of the switches are pressed, the solenoid/solenoid operated 5/2 valve will change over to a 12 combination. When this happens, the double-acting cylinder goes negative closing the barrier.

Solenoid 2 is actuated by SW3 and SW4. The micro-switches are in AND logic. This will cause the solenoid/solenoid operated 5/2 valve to go to a 14 state. When this happens, the cylinder goes positive opening the barrier.

The Electro-pneumatic ladder diagram is shown in Figure 4.72

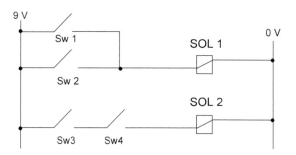

**Figure 4.72** *Ladder diagram for the barrier*

**Symbol diagram for the barrier**

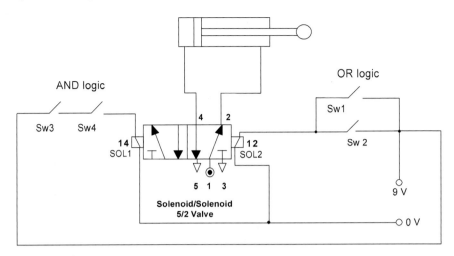

**Figure 4.73** *Symbol diagram for the barrier*

# Designing pneumatic circuits using standard ISO conventions

The recent introduction of a new ISO standard convention for designing pneumatic circuits has simplified the drawing of pneumatic circuits. The technique of drawing signal valves below their point of contact with the piston rod is no longer necessary. Instead you will draw the 3/2 signal valves below the 5/2 valves and cylinder. The location of the signal 3/2 valves are identified by a lettering system. This method does away with the need for signal lines being drawn all over the circuit.

This convention has a few simple rules that must be followed. First components are grouped under headings and located in sections on the diagram. The sections are:

Section 1: Cylinders
Section 2: Speed control
Section 3: Control
Section 4: Signals and logic
Section 5: Power supply

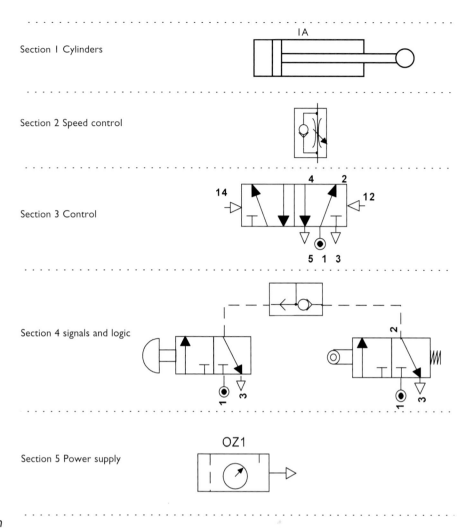

Section 1 Cylinders

Section 2 Speed control

Section 3 Control

Section 4 signals and logic

Section 5 Power supply

**Figure 4.74** *The five sections in ISO circuit design*

## Comparing the new and old drawing conventions

The standard method of drawing a reciprocating motion diagram is shown in Figure 4.75.

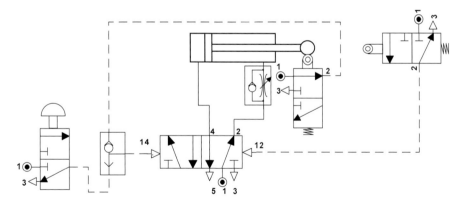

**Figure 4.75** *Standard method of drawing a symbol diagram for reciprocating motion*

In the new ISO convention, you would draw the circuit in sections working upwards from power, signal and logic, control, speed control and cylinders. The circuit diagram is shown in Figure 4.76. The section lines would not appear on the final diagram.

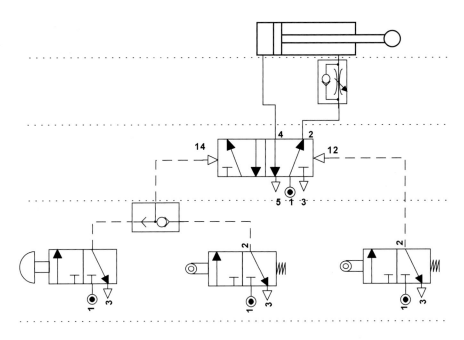

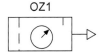

**Figure 4.76** *ISO circuit diagram for reciprocating motion*

The next stage in the new convention is to add identification codes at the end of the cylinder stroke. Upper case letters are used to identify the cylinders and lower case letters are used for the position of the 3/2 signal valves. In figure 4.77 the cylinder is labelled **A** while the position of the signal valves (sensors) are labelled **a0** (negative) and **a1** (positive).

The air signal or commands, as they are known, appearing at the pilot air/pilot air operated 5/2 valve come from the 3/2 signal valves **a0** and **a1**.

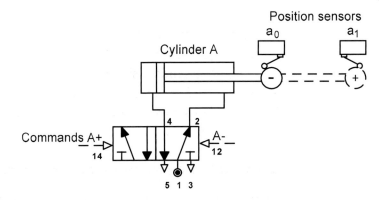

**Figure 4.77** *Functional unit with all codes*

If we complete the circuit diagram for this reciprocating motion circuit **a0** and **a1** are identified as the signal valves that will give you **A+** and **A−**. This is shown in Figure 4.78.

Higher Technology and Design

**206**

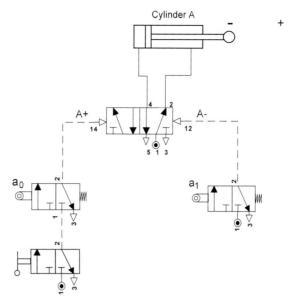

**Figure 4.78** *ISO circuit diagram for this reciprocating motion*

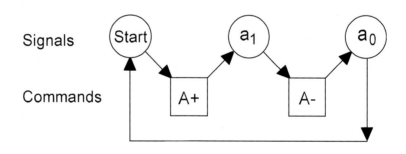

## Sequence of signals and commands

If we consider the circuit diagram shown in Figure 4.78 it is possible to write a sequence of signals and commands for it as follows:

**Figure 4.79** *Sequence of signals and commands*

1. Start (gives you A+)
2. A+ (strikes signal valve a1)
3. a1 (a1 sends a signal to the 5/2 valve to give A−)
4. A− (strikes signal valve a0)
5. a0 (a0 sends a signal to the 5/2 valve to give A+)
6. Return to start

## Sequential control of two cylinders

Figure 4.81 shows the circuit diagram for the control of two cylinder sequential in the sequence A+, B+, A−, B− using ISO conventions. It is useful to draw the sequence of signals and commands as in shown in Figure 4.80.

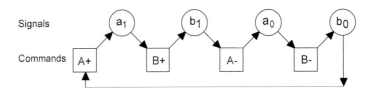

**Figure 4.80** *Sequence of signals and commands for A+, B+, A−, B−*

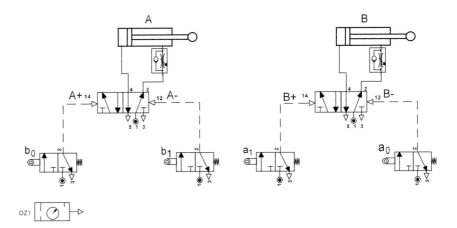

**Figure 4.81** *Circuit diagram for A+, B+, A−, B−*

## Two-cylinder cascade systems using ISO conventions

Cascade is used when the system is inoperable. That is when the signal arriving at one end of the pilot/pilot air operated 5/2 control valve is prevented from changing the valve back due the presence of an air signal at the other end. When this happens it is necessary to use a cascade system.

If you consider a pneumatic system that has two cylinders that have to operate in the sequence: start, A+, A−, B+, B− then the signal that made cylinder A go positive is also preventing it from going negative.

It will be necessary to divide the sequence A+, A−, B+, B−, into two ajectant groups with one cylinder letter appearing no more than once in that group. So A+, A−, B+, B−, would divide into two groups B−, A+ and A−, B+.

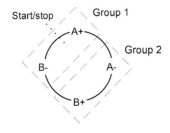

**Figure 4.82** *A+, B− and A−, B+.*

The design of this cascade system can be achieved by dividing it into a number of small steps.

### Step 1. Dividing the sequence of cylinder moves into the two groups

Move clockwise around the circular diagram as shown in Figure 4.82. You will now have two line groups:

Line group I    B−, A+
Line group II   A−, B+

### Step 2. Supplying air to the two line groups

Using a pilot/pilot air operated 5/2 valve to supply the two line groups, you can now draw the group changeover valve called a

**selector valve**. It is this pilot/pilot air operated 5/2 valve that will supply air to no more than one line group at a time. This is shown in figure 4.83.

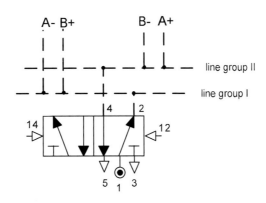

Selector valve 1
(Group I and II changeover valves)

**Figure 4.83** *Drawing the selector valve*

### Step 3. Changing over the selector valve

The changing over of the selector valve is achieved by using two 3/2 signal valves. When the 3/2 valve a1 is pressed, an air signal flows along to the selector valve changing it over to allow air to flow into port 1 and out of port 2. Port 2 is connected to line group I that allows air to flow to A− and B+. When the 3/2 valve b1 is pressed, an air signal flows along to the selector valve changing it over to allow air to flow into port 1 and out of port 4. Port 4 is connected to line group II that allows air to flow to B− and A+. This is shown in Figure 4.84.

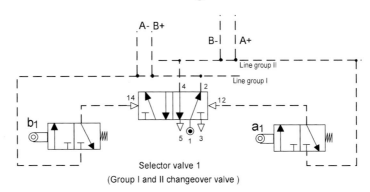

Selector valve 1
(Group I and II changeover valve )

**Figure 4.84** *Changing over the selector valve*

### Step 4. Adding all the components for a two-cylinder cascade

Add all the other components necessary for a two-cylinder cascade system to achieve the sequence B−, A+, A−, B+. This is shown in Figure 4.85.

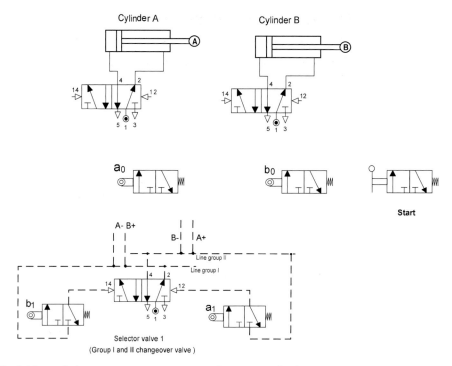

**Figure 4.85** *Adding all the components necessary for a two-cylinder cascade*

### Step 5. Line group I, A−, B+

Pipe the signal air from line group I, to cylinders A and B control valves to give A−, B+. This is shown in Figure 4.86.

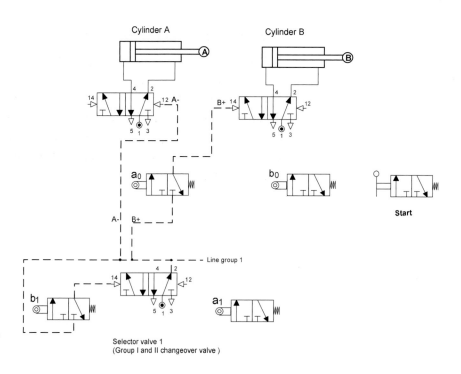

**Figure 4.86** *Line group I A−, B+*

### Step 6. Line group II, B−, A+

Pipe the signal air from line group II to cylinders A and B control valves, to give B- A+. This is shown in figure 4.87.

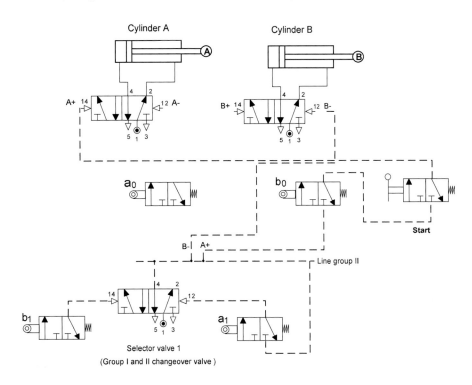

**Figure 4.87** *Line group II, B−, A+*

### Step 7. Combining steps 5 and 6

By combining steps 5 and 6, you can create the circuit that will operate in the sequence A−, B+, B−, A+. The circuit will require a start/stop switch in the form of a roller trip 3/2 valve. This is positioned in the line between valve b0 and cylinder A 5/2 control valve. Once this 3/2 valve is closed, air cannot flow to create A+ and the system stops at this point in the cycle. This is shown in figure 4.88.

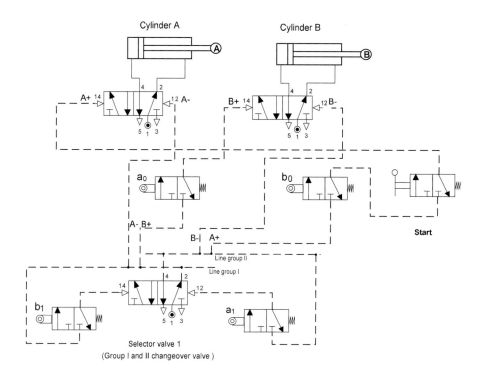

**Figure 4.88** *ISO circuit diagram for two-cylinder cascade A−, B+, B−, A+*

## Three-Cylinder cascade system designed using ISO conventions

Consider the sequential control of three cylinders

- Cylinder A
- Cylinder B
- Cylinder C.

The cylinders are to actuate in the sequence: Start A+ B+ B− C+ C− A−.

The sequence can be described in the form of a circular diagram as shown in Figure 4.89.

The actuation of these cylinders and their return will create a system that is inoperable in a simple sequential order. It will be necessary to design a cascade system where the sequence is grouped in pairs. The designing of this cascade system can be achieved by dividing the system into a number of small steps.

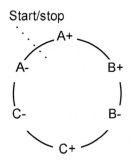

**Figure 4.89** *Circular diagram for the sequence: start, A+, B+, B−, C+, C−, A−*

### Step 1

Divide the sequence of the cylinders into three groups. Moving clockwise around the circular diagram you have the following groups:

Group I    A+ B+
Group II   B− C+
Group III  C− A−

### Step 2

Draw the line groups and the selector valves. For a three-cylinder cascade system you will need two selector valves and three line groups. Connect the line groups to the selector valves as shown in Figure 4.90. By sending a signal to the selector valves, you are able to supply air to one line group at a time.

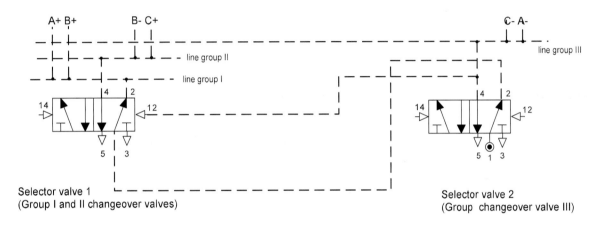

**Figure 4.90** *Piping the selector valves and line groups*

## Explanation of how the selector valves operate

The start of the sequence happens when the last roller trip valve a0 sends a signal to group III to change the selector valve, so that air is permitted to flow through to line group I. Line group I controls the sequence A+ B+ as shown in figure 4.91.

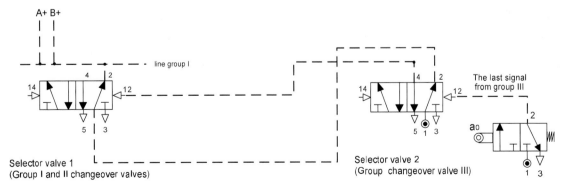

**Figure 4.91** *Selector valves*

## Completing the three-cylinder cascade sequence: A+, B+, B−, C+, C−, A−

Following the same procedure as for the two-cylinder cascade system, pipe the cylinder and valves as shown in figure 4.92.

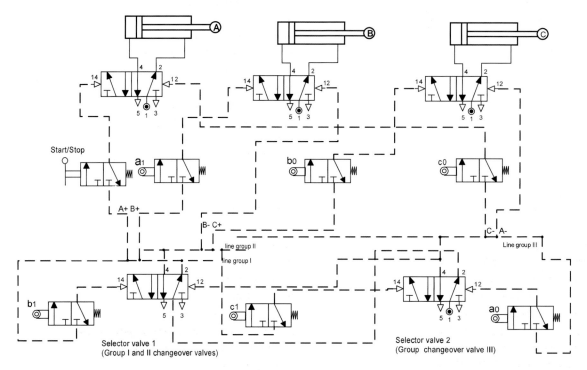

**Figure 4.92** *Three Sequence: A+, B+, B−, C+, C−, A−*

# Index